D1466892

NELSON Language ARTS

WHAT SHOULD I DO?

Gerald Best

Caren Cameron

Maureen Dockendorf

Barb Eklund

Christine Finochio

Ruth Hay

Sharon Jeroski

Eugene Mazur

Mary McCarthy

Maureen Skinner

Senior Program Consultant

Jennette MacKenzie

I(T)P Nelson

an International Thomson Publishing company

Toronto • Albany • Bonn • Boston • Cincinnati • Detroit • London • Madrid • Melbourne
Mexico City • New York • Pacific Grove • Paris • San Francisco • Singapore • Tokyo • Washington

Grade 5 Reviewers:

Lynn Archer
New Westminster, British
Columbia

Faye Brownbridge
Calgary, Alberta

Caren Cameron
Victoria, British Columbia

Katherine Collis
Winnipeg, Manitoba

Dr. Elaine Crocker
St. John's, Newfoundland

Diana Cruise
Winnipeg, Manitoba

Wendy Davidson
Truro, Nova Scotia

Ann Dominick
North York, Ontario

Nancy Farrell
Burnaby, British Columbia

Irene Heffel
Edmonton, Alberta

Helen Hohmann
Edmonton, Alberta

Nancy Leonard
Markham, Ontario

Patti Peroni
Brampton, Ontario

Equity Consultant:
Ken Ramphal

I(T)P® International Thomson Publishing
The ITP logo is a trademark under licence
www.thomson.com

Published by
I(T)P® Nelson
A division of Thomson Canada Limited, 1998
1120 Birchmount Road
Scarborough, Ontario M1K 5G4
www.nelson.com

Printed and bound in Canada
2 3 4 5 6 7 8 9 0 / ML/ 7 6 5 4 3 2 1 0 9 8

Canadian Cataloguing in Publication Data

Main entry under title:

Nelson language arts 5

ISBN 0-17-607525-9 (v. 1 : bound)
ISBN 0-17-607428-7 (v. 1 : pbk.)
Contents: [1] What Should I Do?

1. Readers (Elementary). I. Cameron, Caren, 1949–   .

PE1121.N448 1997   428.6   C97-931515-8

Project Team: Laurel Bishop, Angela Cluer,
Mark Cobham, Kathleen ffolliott, Susan Green,
John McInnes, Marcia Miron, June Reynolds,
Elizabeth Salomons, Theresa Thomas, Jill Young

Art Direction and Production: Liz Harasymczuk

TABLE OF CONTENTS

Unit 3 *Media Moments*

THE NEWS $1.00

Unit 1: *What Should I Do?*

In this unit, you will learn about the many decisions people face in their daily lives. You will read stories, poems, and a quiz that will help you make thoughtful decisions in your own life. You will have opportunities to make connections between the stories and your own decision-making experiences. You will

- find out about the personal choices of others
- learn steps to help you make wise decisions
- think about the decisions you make in your life
- explore thoughts, feelings, and experiences to understand yourself and others
- learn some strategies to help you become a better reader
- make a personal collection about your decisions and choices

Decisions to

Adapted from Kid City *magazine*
Illustrated by Tina Holdcroft

READING TIP

Set a purpose for reading

This selection is a quiz to help you find out what kind of friend you are. As you read, think about how you could use this information to help you make decisions about being a good friend.

There are many decisions you make every day. Some decisions are easy, like *What will I have for breakfast?* or *What shoes should I wear today?* Other decisions are more challenging.

What would you do in situations like these?

Your best friend wants to tell you a secret.

Grow On

Some older students are picking on a younger student. Other kids are watching, or joining in.

A new student takes an empty seat next to you at lunch. Suddenly, a group of popular kids asks you to join their table. There's only one seat there.

9

You haven't seen your best friend all summer. He/she comes back to school with the worst haircut you have ever seen and asks you what you think of it.

Some kids you know are always gossiping about a friend of yours.

To make a decision ...

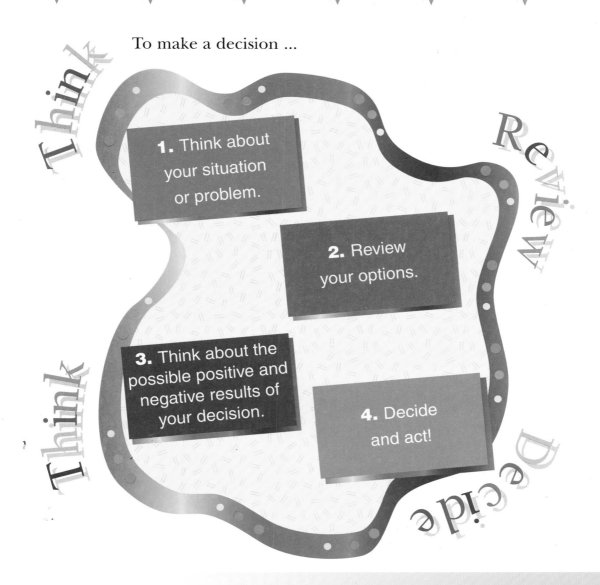

1. Think about your situation or problem.

2. Review your options.

3. Think about the possible positive and negative results of your decision.

4. Decide and act!

Think

Review

Think

Decide

AFTER YOU READ

Think about the decisions you made

Look back at the decisions you made as you read the quiz. Review the four steps for making decisions and record two ways you could use this information to help you with the many choices you make every day.

Fifteen Minutes

Written by Larry Callen
Illustrated by Tadeusz Majewski

READING TIP

Make comparisons

Sometimes decisions need to be made in a hurry. What do you do when you have to make a quick decision? The character in this story has 15 minutes to make a decision. As you read, compare his decision-making process with yours.

1 "You've got fifteen minutes to make up your mind," Mom said. She put the red toothbrush and the green toothbrush on the table, side by side. "If you haven't decided by the time Violet gets here, I'll do the deciding."

2 My old toothbrush had been yellow, and its bristles were soft and bent. These two looked pretty good. Maybe the red would be best. I sat down at the table and studied them.

3 Two minutes later Violet Deever walked in, big smile on her face like she owned the world.

4 "What're you doing?" she asked.

5 "Nothing."

6 She saw the toothbrushes on the table. She reached for one, but I pushed her hand away.

7 "Pat, stop that," she said. "I asked your mother to buy me a toothbrush. One of those is mine."

8 Mom heard her and shouted from the kitchen that I had asked first so I had first choice.

12

LEARNING GOALS

You will

- read a story about a boy who has 15 minutes to make a decision

- make comparisons between this story and your decision-making experiences

1 "Twelve minutes left to decide, Pat."

2 "Oh," said Deever. She sat down on the other side of the table and studied the toothbrushes.

3 "They're both nice, aren't they?" she asked. "You know which one you're going to take yet?"

4 "Whichever one I want," I said. I wasn't going to have her trying to make me take the one *she* didn't want.

5 "Maybe you ought to take the red one," she said, touching the end of the red handle. "It's very nice. The bristles look very straight."

6 Then a sly look crossed her face and I knew she was playing one of her games again. She was going to try and trick me. Well, this time I wasn't going to be tricked. This time I would do the tricking.

7 "Deever, don't touch them. Mom said I had first choice, and that means first touching, too."

8 I looked closely at the green one. If she wanted me to take the red one, she must've seen something special about the green one. Or maybe she just liked the colour best.

1 The green one looked a little bit longer than the red one. But maybe it was just where I was sitting. I moved them closer together to compare size.

2 "It doesn't seem right that you can touch them and I can't," she said.

"One of them is going to be mine, isn't it? Well, I don't want you touching my toothbrush. A toothbrush is a very personal thing, Pat. People don't go around touching other people's toothbrushes."

3 All her talk was getting in the way of my deciding which one I wanted.

4 "Mom, make Violet stop talking. I can't think when she is talking."

5 Deever looked at her wristwatch. "You've got only ten more minutes to decide, Pat."

6 Now she was really trying to get me confused.

7 "I haven't really decided yet, but I think that I might just take the green one," I said.

8 The expression on her face didn't change a whit. Not an eyelid flickered. She stared me in the eye, daring me to guess what she was thinking.

9 "You have nine minutes left, Pat," she said.

But I wasn't going to be rushed into anything. I stood up and went to the kitchen for a glass of water. Mom was slicing tomatoes and cucumbers and celery for a salad.

10 "Mom, do I *have* to decide in fifteen minutes?"

"Decide about what, dear?"

"Aw, Mom. You know. The toothbrush. Violet is sitting right there, trying to get me to take the one she doesn't want."

Now Mom was washing lettuce at the sink.

"I can't see what difference the colour of a toothbrush makes, Pat. Just pick one and be done with it."

But she didn't understand. I went back into the dining room. And I saw right away that Deever had moved both brushes. The green one had been closest to where I was sitting. Now the red one was closest.

"A fly lit on it," she said.

"What?"

"I wouldn't take the green one if I were you, Pat. While you were gone a fly lit on it. Maybe it laid some eggs. How would you like brushing your teeth with a bunch of fly eggs?"

"I'm not listening to that kind of stuff, Deever. I'm picking the one I want. Not the one you *don't* want."

"Know what colour fly eggs are, Pat?"

I was looking at the toothbrushes. The bristles of both were snowy white. It looked like there might be a fleck of something on the bristles of the green one, but it surely wasn't fly eggs. Maybe dust is all.

"They are green. That's what colour fly eggs are."

I flicked the bristles of the green toothbrush with my finger and whatever was on them disappeared. But if I took the green one, I would wash it with scalding water anyway.

I'd already wasted more than half of my time and I still didn't know which one I wanted. I like red. It's a bright, kind of loud colour. I wouldn't want red clothes, except maybe a tie. Dad's got a red sport coat that he wore one time only, and then swore he would never wear again because everybody kept making jokes about it. But a toothbrush is different. I never heard a toothbrush joke in my whole life.

"Pat, have you ever broken a tooth?" asked Deever.

I was just getting started on my thinking and she got me distracted again.

Mom's not going to fool around. At the end of the fifteen minutes, she's going to decide who gets what colour.

"The reason I asked, Pat, is that when you break a tooth, it means a friend will die. I had that happen to me when I was only six years old. It wasn't exactly a person-friend. It was a hamster. But it broke my heart. You know what my hamster's name was, Pat?"

"Deever, will you please let me think?"

She says I ought to take the red one. She knows I'm not going to take the one she wants me to. That means she knows I'll take the green one. And that means she wants the red one. If she just keeps quiet a little bit longer, I'll have this thing puzzled out.

"Red is a very lucky colour, Pat. Did you know it can even help you if you have a poor memory? All you have to do is tie a red string around a finger on your left hand—"

"And remember why you tied it there," I snarled. She just wouldn't shut up.

"Mom, what time is it?"

"You have five minutes left, Pat," said Deever. "You are surely taking a long time to make up your mind."

1   She got up and went into the kitchen. I could hear low voices and laughter. Then she came back, crunching on a celery stick.

2   *She says I should take the red one. But she also knows I won't do it, because she is telling me to do it. But if I'm smart enough to figure that out, then I'll take the red one, and she'll be left with the green one.*

3   *Suppose she's figured out that I'll figure it out. Which one does she really want, then?*

4   I was getting confused.

5   I looked at her. She was still chewing on the celery. Was she trying to say something to me with that green stick? She smiled at me, still chewing.

6   *Maybe I ought to get back to thinking about which one I want, instead of which one she wants. The green one is pretty. Kind of a grass green. I've got to get that business about fly eggs out of my mind. That's just trickery.*

7   *Lots of nice-looking things are green. Lawns are green. Leaves are green. Olives. Emeralds. Watermelons.*

8   *Watermelons.*

9   *But the sweet part on the inside is red.*

10   "Do you know anything about rotten garbage, Pat? It's ugly and slimy and probably full of fly eggs. Did I ever tell you that once I had a possum for a pet? Possums eat garbage. Did you know that? And they have funny green stuff growing all over their teeth."

I used to like brushing my teeth. Made them feel clean. And I like the taste of toothpaste. They put something in it that tickles your tongue. Sometimes when we run out of toothpaste, I brush with salt, and I even like the taste of that. But I wasn't looking forward to brushing my teeth ever again.

"What time do you think it is, Pat?" she asked.

"All right, Deever. Which one do you *really* want?"

"Oh, I don't have a real preference. I just thought the red one would be nice for you."

I balled my fist. I knew she wasn't going to tell me the truth.

"You're just saying that, right? I'll take the red one, and then you will get the green one, which is the one you really want. I know what you're trying to do, Deever."

She tilted her head, lifted her eyebrows, and kind of sniffed, like she was saying I had a right to my opinion even if I was wrong.

"I'll be back in two minutes," Mom said.

I whirled on Deever. I wanted to yell at her to go away, but she wasn't smiling like she was winning the war or anything. There was a kind of hurt look on her face.

"I thought I had been helping you, Pat," she said.

"Deever, a guy doesn't need help to pick the right colour for a toothbrush."

"All right, then. I won't say another word." She sat back in her chair and looked at me. The hurt look stayed on her face. Now she was trying to make me feel guilty.

"One minute!" called Mom.

Which one? Red one? Green one? Ruby one? Emerald one? Somehow I knew she wanted the red one. I just knew it.

I could hear Mom stirring around in the kitchen. She was going to come marching out here any second.

"All right. I've decided," I said.

I stretched my hand out over the toothbrushes. I paused over the red one and looked at Deever's face, but I couldn't tell a thing. Then I moved my hand over the green one. Still nothing.

I scooped my hand down and grabbed the green one, watching her from the corner of my eye. Her face lit up.

"Good!" she said.

Now I knew. I dropped the green toothbrush and grabbed the red one. I pulled it close to me. This time I had won.

"Time's up!" yelled Mom.

I grinned at Deever and waited for her smile to fade. But it didn't happen.

She reached out in her dainty way. With two fingers she plucked the green toothbrush from the table.

"Wonderful!" she said. "Green is my favourite colour."

AFTER YOU READ

Find similarities and differences

Think of a time when you had an experience similar to Pat's. Make a list of all the things that made your decision difficult and a list of what made Pat's decision difficult. How are your lists the same? different?

Liam McLafferty's
CHOICE

Written by Alexis O'Neill
Illustrated by Laszlo Gal

READING TIP

Think about your experiences

Sometimes we make decisions that are hard for other people
to understand. Think about a time when you made a decision
that others could not figure out. What happened? As you
read, stop after each decision that the character makes and
try to figure out why he made that particular choice.

1 No young lad in Ireland made worse choices than Liam
McLafferty of Rosmuck.

2 When his brother asked, "Would you rather have this
apple or that apple?" Liam chose the one that spoiled first.

3 When his mother asked, "Would you like to spread
manure or milk the cow?" Liam chose to spread the
manure.

4 When his father asked, "Would you like to come with
me to the Galway fair or stay and mind the wee ones?" Liam
chose to stay.

5 When his schoolmaster asked, "Would you like to
stand in the corner or sit beside rough Kieran O'Keefe?"
Liam chose to sit beside rough Kieran.

6 Try as he might, Liam could not make a good choice.
On market day, his mother endeavoured to teach him.

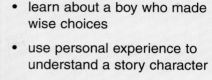

1 "There now, Liam," she said. "Look at those three pigs. Which should we take home with us?"

2 Liam examined them closely, as all farmers did. Each pig was round and noisy. Each one would make a fine dinner. But each one looked him square in the face.

3 "I'll take that sack of potatoes," said Liam, and he covered his eyes as he walked away from his mother's side.

4 One night, Liam heard his parents whispering by the hearth. "Liam is our oldest lad," his father said, "yet how can we leave our field to him? Sure, the land will be lost if Liam puts his hand to it."

5 Liam's heart broke. Before the sun rose, he walked past the fields to the sea to think. As it happened, he spied two figures upon the beach in the rosy dawn.

1 "Lend a hand, would you?" called a beautiful colleen as she tugged on her great green cloak, which was caught in the rocks.

2 "Lend a hand, would you?" croaked an old woman as she tried to hobble up a narrow path in her black shawl and red skirt.

3 Now, any other young man would have raced to help the beautiful girl. But not Liam McLafferty. Without so much as a second thought, he raced to the side of the wrinkled old woman.

4 At the top of the path, the old woman turned to him. "Tell me, Liam McLafferty, *why* did you choose to help me when you might have had that lovely colleen on your arm instead?"

5 Liam was stunned. In all his life, no one had ever asked him why he had chosen the way he had. The wind blew soft against his face as he stood above the rolling sea.

6 "Now that you ask," he said, "I thought that a young colleen might be able to free her own self from the rocks. I thought that an old woman might have more use of my arm climbing up a craggy hill."

7 "And the apple?" asked the woman as she rested against a rock.

"The riper the apple, the more ready the seeds are for planting," he said without stopping to wonder how she knew about the spoiled apple.

"The manure?" she asked.

"Why, it helps things to grow," Liam replied.

"And why stay with the wee ones when you could have gone to the fair?" she persisted.

"They need my stories so they might tell their own someday," he said. Then he thought about his other choices. "I sat beside rough Kieran, for who else would befriend him? As for the potatoes, don't they nourish a family without harming a pig?"

The old woman nodded as she stood on the path. Then quick as a hare, she spun around until she was but a blur of black and red. When the spinning stopped, there before Liam stood the queen of the fairy kingdom.

"Liam, for listening to your heart's own good sense above others' opinions, you may choose your reward."

Och! Poor Liam! Another choice to make!

Think hard, he whispered to himself. What would a smart Irish lad choose? A room of gold! he thought. Now, wouldn't that make Da happy. Oh, better! A village full of

friends! Now, wouldn't that make Ma proud. Liam thought these things, but he said nothing. He was afraid of being laughed at once again.

The fairy queen tapped her delicate foot. "Come, now, Liam. *No* choice is a choice, too."

Liam found his voice. "All I ask is a wee dram of knowledge and the wisdom to make good choices," he said, then cringed, afraid that the fairy queen would mock him.

"'Tis yours, as it has always been. Trust it," she said and disappeared.

When Liam arrived at his cottage, there on his cot was a wee slip of parchment. On it were two words: TELL THEM.

The village soon spilled with tales of Liam McLafferty and the fairy queen. The laughter followed. What young man with any sense at all would choose a wisp of parchment over a fortune in gold?

Och. But Liam knew the half of it. For as he soon discovered, the words he carried with him gave him courage. With each choice he made, he explained the whys and wherefores of it. And there wasn't a reason that didn't make good sense to the others.

As it happened, the young colleen in the great green cape soon became his wife. With her love and his heart's own good sense to guide him, he made his father's land prosper. Villagers came to him for advice, and his hearth never lacked for a friendly face.

Truth be told, as the years passed, all the villagers came to agree on one thing: no young lad in the whole long history of Ireland ever made better choices than Liam McLafferty of Rosmuck.

AFTER YOU READ

Build your decision-making skills

Liam was given a slip of paper that read "TELL THEM." How did this change affect the way other people reacted to his decisions? How can you use this advice to help you with your decision-making skills?

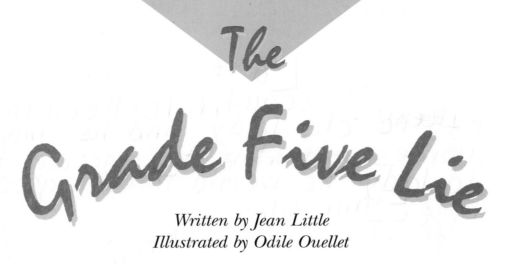

The Grade Five Lie

Written by Jean Little
Illustrated by Odile Ouellet

READING TIP

Make predictions

Use the title, the illustrations, and any special print features
(such as italics or capitalized words) to predict what the story
will be about. Use the information from the story to confirm
or revise your predictions.

I was eating my porridge when Hugh, hurrying too fast,
fell down the back stairs. Before Mother could get up, he
limped in, sniffling slightly, and displayed a bumped elbow
for her inspection. Mother examined it gravely.

"A slight hematoma," she said in a serious voice. "And
an abrasion almost invisible to the naked eye. You'll live."

Hugh, who always recovered with the speed of light
and who won Mother's admiration with his bravery,
chuckled at the impressive words.

"What does that mean?" he asked.

"A little bruise and a scrape I can hardly see."

I glowered at my oatmeal. Why did she have to smile
at him like that? He was not so special. I searched my mind
for something terrible he had done that I could tell her
about.

LEARNING GOALS

You will

- read a story about a girl who discovers the power of words

- sketch and write your predictions to help you understand the story

"Jean, hurry up or you'll be late," Grandma said.

I did not want to go to school. We were going to have another arithmetic test, and I still did not know my times tables. If only I could fall down and break my leg....

Four-year-old Pat grinned at me.

"Huwwy up, Jean," she parroted. "You'll be late."

I wanted to slap the wide smile off her silly little face. Instead I scooped up a few drops of milk on the tip of my spoon and let fly. The tiny bit of milk splashed her on the nose. I laughed. Before anyone could stop her, Pat grabbed up her mug filled to the brim with milk and sent its entire contents sloshing over me, soaking me to the skin.

The next thing I knew, I was back upstairs changing out of my wet serge dress, cotton petticoat, long brown stockings, and underwear into clean dry clothes. Not only was this going to make me really late, but Mother handed me the knitted suit Aunt Gretta had made for my tenth birthday. The ribbed blue skirt was sewn onto a sleeveless cotton vest. Over it went a horizontally striped blue and pink sweater with short sleeves. Nobody else in Miss Marr's class had a homemade knitted suit anything like it.

"I can't wear it," I said in anguished tones.

"It's lovely," my mother said calmly. "Gretta worked hard to make it for you. Don't be ridiculous. Of course you will wear it."

In ten minutes I was gobbling toast and honey, gulping down milk, and hating my cheerful little sister who was the cause of all the trouble and who got to stay home and be spoiled by everybody.

When I reached the street, it was ominously quiet. I really was going to be late, and it was all Pat's fault. I ran the first three blocks, but slowed down when I got a stitch in my side. There was still not a single child in sight.

As I passed St. John's School, I could hear the grade four class singing "God Save the King." I sent the small building a look of longing. Mr. Johnston had not had these horrid arithmetic tests.

Then I stood stock still. When I got to school, Miss Marr would tell me to put my name on the board to stay after four. I didn't mind staying late—lots of the others got detentions—I wasn't sure what to write, though I had a strong suspicion that you did not write out your whole name. Did you just write your initials? Or one initial and your surname? Or your first name and your last initial?

I had to get it right. The others still called me names when no teacher was near enough to hear. The only game I had ever been invited to play was Crack the Whip, and they always made me go on the end. Then, when the big girl at the front swung everybody around in a long *Crack!*, I ended up flying through the air and landing with a jarring crash on my hands and knees. As I picked myself up, I'd try to look as though I thought crash-landings were fun. Nobody was fooled.

If I wrote my name up there differently than the others did, they would have a new thing to tease me about. I could hear the jeering voices already.

"You're not just cross-eyed, you're so *dumb* you don't even know how to write your name on the board!"

I stood there, thinking hard. How could I save myself? Once in a while, when a child brought a note from home, he got out of putting his name on the board. Well, my mother would not write me a note.

Perhaps, if your parents were not at home, and some emergency cropped up and you had to deal with it, Miss Marr just might let you sit down without asking for a note. It would have to be a desperate emergency....

I began to walk again, taking my time. I had to invent the most convincing lie of my life. Bit by bit, I worked it out. As I imagined how it must have happened, it grew so real that I began to believe it myself. I had every detail ready as I turned the last corner. Then I began to run.

I knew it was essential that I be out of breath when I arrived.

I dashed up the stairs, puffing hard. I opened the door, said a private prayer for help, and entered the grade five classroom. Miss Marr was at her desk. Out of the corner of my eye, I could see monitors collecting the test papers. So far so good.

"Jean," said my teacher, "you're late."

"Yes," I panted, facing her and opening my eyes wide so that I would look innocent and pitiful. "I know. I couldn't help it."

"Why are you late?" she asked.

I took a deep breath.

"Well, I was all ready in plenty of time. But just as I was going out the door, the telephone rang. I knew I should not go back to answer it, but you know my mother and father are both doctors and I was afraid it might be an emergency."

Miss Marr opened her mouth to ask a question, but I

rushed on, not giving her time to get a word in edgewise.

"The trouble was, you see, that nobody was home but me. So I took the receiver off the hook and I said, 'Dr. Littles' residence.'"

Everybody was listening now, even the boys who never paid attention. I kept going.

"MY DAUGHTER IS DYING! MY DAUGHTER IS DYING!"

I saw my teacher jump as I shrieked the words at the top of my lungs. Her eyes were wide with shock. The class gasped. I did not stop for effect. I could not give the teacher time to interrupt.

"It was a man's voice. He sounded frantic with worry. 'I'm sorry,' I told him, 'my parents are out. If you call back, they should be home in one hour.' 'No! Please, don't hang up,' he begged. 'You must come and save her life. If I wait for your parents, she will surely die.' 'Well, I guess if she is dying, I'd better come. Where do you live?' I asked him. '111 King Street,' he told me."

Miss Marr did not even try to ask a question as I paused to catch my breath. The entire class was sitting spellbound. The silence was absolute. Not a desk seat squeaked. Not a giggle broke the hush.

"I hurried in and got the right medicine from the office and then I ran out the door. I didn't go the long way around by the Norwich Street bridge. I was afraid it would take too long. I went down London Road and across some stepping stones down there. When I got to King Street, there was the house. It was a log cabin with wind whistling through the cracks. And as I came up to it, I saw the door was standing open and there were a bunch of people in the doorway and they were all crying. 'What's wrong?' I asked them. 'You are too late,' they sobbed. 'She's dead already.'"

This time, as I snatched a breath, Miss Marr choked back a small sound. She made no attempt to stem the flood of my story. I pressed on.

"'Oh, I am so sorry,' I told them. 'Take me to see her.' So they took me into the cabin and there lay the girl on a trundle bed. Her face was blue and her eyes had rolled up till you could just see white and her teeth were clenched. And her fingers and toes all curled over backward."

I watched Miss Marr carefully at this point, because I was not absolutely sure what a dead person looked like. The last bit worried me especially. I had heard someone say that when people died, they turned their toes up. That could only mean that their toes curled over backward, but I was not sure about the fingers.

Miss Marr's face quivered a little and her mouth twitched, but she did not speak. I hurried, eager to finish. It would be a relief to sit down. Even so, in spite of myself, I kept putting in extra bits as they occurred to me.

"'She's not quite dead,' I cried. 'She's just on the point of death. I think I can save her.' I hit her chin and her mouth opened. I poured in the medicine. She fluttered her lashes and turned a normal colour and said weakly, 'Where am I?' I turned and hurried toward the door. But before I could escape, all the weeping people went down on their knees and grabbed hold of my skirt and they said, 'You saved her life! We want to give you a reward. Gold, silver, a bag of emeralds, a horse that will come when you whistle ... tell us the one thing you want more than anything else in the world and you can have it.'"

I paused for effect this time. I knew no one would break the hush. I wanted my teacher to take in the next bit.

"'The one thing I want more than anything else in the world,' I told them, 'is to be on time for school.' So they let me go and I ran down the hill and across the stepping stones. When I got to the third last stone, though, I slipped and fell in the river and cut my knee. I had to get to shore, go home and bandage my knee, and put on dry clothes. Then I hurried here as fast as I could. And that is why I am late."

There was a stunned silence in the classroom. Miss Marr and I stared at each other for a long, long minute. I waited for her to tell me to write my name on the board. Instead she pointed her finger at my desk. Speaking extremely slowly and wearily, she said, "Take ... your ... seat. Just ... take ... your ... seat."

I tried to keep a solemn expression on my face. But it was hard not to grin. I sat down and did not turn my head as a buzz of whispers broke out behind me. I had missed the arithmetic test. I had not had to write my name on the board. And I had kept every single person transfixed with my exciting story.

At least three blissful minutes went by before I realized I had no cut on my knee and no bandage, either. Not only that, but I could not remember whether I had told her which knee I was supposed to have cut.

She had believed me. I was sure of that. Yet any second she was going to discover that I had told her a stupendous lie.

I hooked one knee over the other and clasped my hands around the knee on top. I spent the entire morning that way. When I was required to write, I used only one hand. Miss Marr did not ask me a direct question. When recess time came and she said, "Class, stand," I stayed where I was.

"Jean, aren't you going out for recess?" she asked when the others had marched out and there I still sat.

"Oh, Miss Marr," I said in my smallest, most pathetic voice, "I am so tired from saving that girl's life that I have to stay in and have a rest."

Still clutching my knee with both hands, I laid my head down on my desk and shut my eyes.

She did not say a word.

At noon, when she had her back turned, I ran out of the classroom, dashed home, sneaked Band-Aids from my parents' office, and plastered them over both knees, to be on the safe side. When I returned to school, Miss Marr smiled and did not ask why both my knees were bandaged.

I sat through the afternoon thinking over what had happened. Did she really guess? The other kids did not seem to have figured out that I had lied. One girl had even smiled at me, as though she might be my friend. Nobody in my class had called me cross-eyed. A boy in grade seven had, though. If only I could shut him up the way I had hushed everybody that morning.

Then I remembered Hugh's knee. That night I asked Mother, "What are the long words for what's wrong with my eyes?"

I was standing beside her chair. She looked up at me.

"Why?" she asked.

"I want to know, that's all. They call me cross-eyed. I want to know the long words, the ones doctors use."

She rhymed off a whole list.

"Say it again. Slowly."

"Strabismus, nystagmus, corneal opacities, and eccentric pupils."

I practised.

The next day I was late coming out of school. The same grade-seven boy was waiting for me. He had his first snowball ready.

"Cross-eyed, cross-eyed," he chanted and waited for me to start running so that he could chase me, pelting me with hard-packed snowballs.

I turned on him instead.

"I am not cross-eyed," I said in a strong, clear voice. "I have corneal opacities and eccentric pupils."

I glared at him as I spoke and my eyes were as crossed as ever. But he was so surprised that he stood there, his mouth gaping open like a fish's.

Then I turned my back and walked away. Perhaps his aim was off because he was so used to firing his missiles at a running target. But the first snowball flew past me harmlessly. The second exploded with a smack against a nearby tree.

I kept walking, chin in the air.

In the last two days, I had learned a lot about the power of words. Snowballs would hit me again and I would run away and cry. I would be late and, eventually, I would even have to write my name on the board.

But I had found out what mere words could do. I would not forget.

AFTER YOU READ

Record your predictions and findings

Use a chart like the one below to record your predictions and findings. Using the information from the story, record your responses in the three columns.

My Predictions	Evidence That Confirmed My Predictions	Evidence That Made Me Reject My Predictions

About the Author

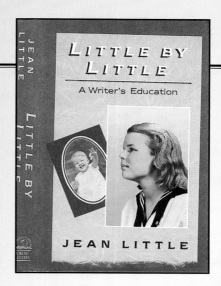

As an author, Jean Little makes decisions every day. When she first began writing books for children, she decided that telling about the experiences of real kids was very important to her. She had noticed that most books about characters with disabilities ended with the characters cured. Jean knew that, in real life, most disabilities do not disappear. She decided that characters in her books would have all kinds of different life experiences, and they would meet any challenges with humour and emotions such as anger, fear, and courage.

When Jean writes each book, she makes decisions about all the elements of the story—from how the plot develops and what her characters are like, to where to put commas and periods.

Since Jean has impaired vision, she makes all of these writing decisions with technology adapted to her needs.

When she first started writing, she dictated each book—punctuation and all—onto many audio cassettes. Then the tapes were typed word for word to become a manuscript. Next Jean's editor would read the manuscript back to her and both would suggest changes. One of Jean's novels took seven years to write using this method! Now Jean uses a talking computer: she types her book into a computer and the computer reads back to her what she has written.

It's Your Decision

READING TIP

Notice text features

Make a list of the things that you already know about poems. Look at the next four poems. What do you notice that is the same about poetry and the other kinds of writing in this unit? What do you notice that is different?

LEARNING GOALS

You will

- find out about the personal choices of others
- learn about special features in poems

No matter which way you turn there's always something you're not facing

Written by Robert Priest

I Do Not Wish to Go to School

Written by Jack Prelutsky
Illustrated by Sean Dawdy

"I do not wish to go to school,"
insisted Sarah Sue,
"and Mother, if you make me,
I will eat a worm or two."

"Do you mean worms like these, my dear?"
her mother firmly said.
"I got them in the garden,
they're extremely long and red.

"They're both the very juiciest
and plumpest I could find."
"I'm off for school," said Sarah Sue,
"for I have changed my mind!"

Karate Kid

Written by Jane Yolen
Illustrated by Janet Wilson

I am wind,
I am wall,
I am wave,
I rise, I fall.
I am crane
In lofty flight,
Training that
I need not fight.

I am tiger,
I am tree,
I am flower,
I am knee,
I am elbow,
I am hands
Taught to do
The heart's commands.

Not to bully,
Not to fight,
Dragon left
And leopard right.
Wind and wave,
Tree and flower,
Chop.
     Kick.
        Peace.
          Power.

Quitter

Written by Janet Wong
Illustrated by Barbara Spurll

Coach calls me a quitter.

He mutters it under his breath
loud enough for me to hear,
but quiet enough
so no one knows
when I prove him wrong.

AFTER YOU READ

Give reasons for your choice

Have you learned anything new about poetry that you can add to
your list? Each of the poets uses a different way to tell a poem.
Which style of poem do you like best? Give reasons for your
choice.

Zora Hurston and the Chinaberry Tree

Written by William Miller
Illustrated by Bernadette Lau

READING TIP

Make personal responses

As you read this story, pause after each page and think
about your ideas, feelings, visual images, and opinions.
Record your responses in a chart like the one below.

Ideas	Images
Feelings	**Opinions**

Zora Hurston loved the chinaberry tree.

Her mother taught her to climb it, one
branch at a time.
From the tree, she could see as far
as the lake, as far as the horizon.

Zora dreamed of seeing the cities beyond
the horizon, of living there one day.

But only boys fished in the lake,
only men travelled to the cities.
Zora watched with envy as the wagons
rattled down the dusty roads.

Her father told her to wear a dress,
to leave tree-climbing to wild boys
who had no better way to spend their time.

He warned her about girls who didn't obey
their parents, girls who didn't grow up to
be young ladies.

But Zora only listened to her mother.

She taught Zora that everything had a voice:
the trees and rushing wind, the stars
in the midnight sky.

She taught Zora that the world belonged
to her, even the lake and far-off horizon.

So Zora went everywhere.

She walked into the town store and watched
while the men played checkers.

LEARNING GOALS

You will

- read a story about a girl who learns to listen to her own voice

- note how the author makes you respond to Zora's story

She asked questions and more questions
until the men taught her how to play.

She followed boys to the edge of campfires,
listened while their fathers sang.

Zora learned about Africa, the place where
she and her people came from.

In Africa they had been kings and queens,
builders of cities that stood for thousands of years.

One morning Zora's mother didn't feel well.

She told Zora not to worry.
She told Zora to go outside and play,
to climb her favourite tree.

But Zora couldn't play. She saw how tired
her mother was. She saw the pain in her eyes.

Day after day, Zora sat beside her mother's bed
telling her the stories she had heard
beside the campfires.

Her mother smiled and asked Zora to always
remember what she had learned.

Stories, she said, kept their people alive.
As long as they were told, Africa would live
in their hearts.
Zora promised to remember.

Zora's mother slowly got worse.
Men and women came to sit up with her
through the long, hot nights.

Zora was sitting in the parlour when her
father told her she would not see her
mother again.

Zora felt as if she had died.

She watched while the women cried and the men
stared at their Sunday shoes.
But then she could sit still no more.

Zora ran from the house, ran all the way
to the chinaberry tree.

She climbed the first branch and the next,
climbed almost to the top.

A sparrow sang to her in a voice like her
mother's. The sparrow told her
not to give up, to climb even higher.

From the top of the tree Zora saw again
the world her mother had given her:
the lake filled with fish, the cities where she would
tell people all she had learned.

Zora promised her mother that she would
never stop climbing,
would always reach for the newborn sky,
always jump at the morning sun!

AFTER YOU READ

Think about your responses

Review the information recorded in your Personal Response chart. What parts of the story caused you to record the most ideas, the clearest visual images, the strongest feelings and opinions? What did the author do to make you respond in this way?

Floodwaters

Written by Jill Rubalcaba
Illustrated by Stephen Snider

READING TIP

Make predictions

The family in this story is forced to abandon their home because of a flood. Make a list of the things that you think a family would decide to bring with them if they had to leave in a hurry.

"That was Joe Poke," Papa said, hanging up the telephone. "He says the levee won't hold the water back much longer." I started for Beannie's cat carrier. Papa and Mama looked long at one another, having one of their conversations without the vexation of words.

Mama broke free first, snatching at things till she built up an armful. Then she started up the stairs to the second floor, yelling to Papa over her shoulder, "Just want to get Granny Dell's wedding veil, the photo albums, and Jodie's baby book. Won't be a minute."

The wedding veil and a rosewood bentwood rocker were all Mama had left of the Dell side of the family. I didn't take to the veil, but the bentwood was a different matter altogether. It had carried me on many a sea voyage, rolling long and high, the way I imagined an ocean vessel might. If it were me doing the choosing, it'd be the bentwood's salvation and not the veil's.

LEARNING GOALS

You will

- learn about difficult decisions a family made during a flood
- make predictions based on your personal experiences

49

I picked up Beannie's cat carrier; Papa had dug it out of the barn when talk of the flood started. We'd been getting ready in stages for days now. I followed behind Mama, picking up her overflow. The carrier bumped up the stairs, and she didn't even holler once about nicking her woodwork. I knew right then things must be bad.

"Beannie!" I called. The drumming of rain on the tin roof was all that answered.

"When those sirens go off, I don't care what's left to be done, you get in the pickup, you hear?" Papa hollered as he scooped armfuls of stuff and followed us upstairs two steps at a time.

Mama stuffed things into pillowcases and stacked them by the bedroom door for Papa to take out to the truck.

"Beannie."

Thunder rolled off in the distance. Papa ran downstairs with Mama's sacks and back up with his arms loaded with whatever he could lay his hands on.

"What on earth you tote this up here for?" Mama held up a half-empty bag of potato chips.

They set to laughing. Their laughter sounded brittle like it might break. Mama couldn't stop, and Papa put his arm around her. She leaned into him, wiped her eyes, and said, "No time for such nonsense." But she didn't stop leaning, and he didn't let go.

"Meow! Meow!" Beannie cried from the attic stairs, just as if she were calling, "I'm here. Up here."

I started up the stairs, and Beannie started down. That's when the sirens went off. We both froze, listening to the wailing. Then the fire whistle started up, climbing to a woeful pitch. Beannie's tail went straight up, and she disappeared in a flash. I raced up the stairs after her, but Papa caught me by the ankle.

"No time."

"But Papa, Beannie!"

"I'm sorry, Jodie."

He threw me over his shoulder. I started kicking. I hung on to the doorframe shouting for Beannie. Papa pulled me free and started to run. Passing through the kitchen doorway, the cat carrier hit the moulding and snapped my wrist. It hurt something awful, but I held on. Held on even though Beannie wasn't in it.

Papa plopped me onto Mama's lap in the pickup. Even though I'm much too old to be sitting there, I stayed, watching our house through the rain. I tried to see into the black attic windows for some sign of Beannie.

I kept watching even when I wasn't sure which dark smudge on the sheet of rain was our house. Mama couldn't get me to let go of the empty cat carrier, so she held it on her lap, too.

The headlights lit up the water running across the steps of the houses we passed. Tan water rippled down the

street. At first I thought I heard the wind coming up. Then I realized it wasn't the wind at all, but the roaring of the water coming for us. I felt a panic rising up in me.

I closed my eyes, aiming to shut out the flood, but it didn't do any good. Dogs were barking, cows were lowing, and even the roosters were crowing. That, with the rain and the rushing water, made a racket scarier than watching the water inching upward. So I kept my eyes open the rest of the way to the shelter.

Turning into the armoury, Papa skidded in the mud. The place looked like a fortress. It was sandbagged clear around even though it was on high ground. Some prankster had spray-painted on the wall, "The Mississippi. Coming soon to a town near you." Mama started in with that same funny, brittle laugh, only this time Papa didn't join her.

Inside, cots were lined up in long rows, and folks were setting up their stuff and snapping sheets out over the grey canvas. Some had family pictures propped up on

boxes standing next to their cots. An old lady and her granddaughter were playing go fish on the cot next to mine.

I couldn't sleep much that night. Beannie had always shared my pillow. And the sounds were all wrong. Babies were crying and clusters of men whispered rumours of houses being swept clear off their foundations. Those snatches of lost houses scared me the most because of Beannie. What if our house were to float away? How would I find Beannie?

When I finally fell asleep, I dreamed of Beannie floating through town on an orange crate wailing, "Meow, meow. I'm here. Over here." My pillow was cold and wet when I woke up.

"Where's Papa?" I asked, looking at his made-up cot.

"He's gone to see about borrowing a boat from Joe Poke so he can check on the house."

"We can rescue Beannie," I said.

Mama stroked my head and said, "Jodie, there's not much hope of Beannie surviving."

"Of course she will, Mama." I'd made up my mind I wasn't giving up on Beannie, say what they liked.

When Papa came back, I was dressed and ready. He looked at the carrier in my hand and shook his head. "I'm afraid you won't have any use for that."

"Maybe not, but I'm bringing it anyhow." I used the same firm tone Papa did when he didn't want to argue. He must've heard it, because he just shook his head and said no more.

Papa steered Joe Poke's aluminum fishing outboard past Lulu's, where Mama got her hair done. The water was over the top of the front door. The whole of Grainville was neck deep in the muddy Mississippi.

The bullfrogs were croaking so loud we had to shout to be heard over their rejoicing. Not that we were saying much. When Cora Lynn's piano floated by, Mama just pointed.

Everything imaginable was floating by us: washtubs, workbenches, carpeting. And snakes were everywhere. When we floated onto our street, I felt like I'd entered another world. The very street I'd pedalled my bicycle on a hundred times before was missing beneath an ocean of water. All the houses and barns on our street had little more than their roofs showing. None of us could take our eyes off what had been our house.

I started recognizing things floating past. Some were things Papa had carried up to the second floor yesterday. He cut the motor and let the boat drift up to the house. No one said a word.

I guess I hadn't noticed until that moment that the rain had stopped. I feared my heart would stop, too. Papa paddled us around the roof of the dead house.

Mama squeezed my hand. "Maybe she got out. Cats can swim, you know."

Papa frowned at Mama. I know how he hated sugarcoating things. He was as gentle as a butterfly beat, yet

he never spoke anything but the truth. He believed it was the least hurtful in the long run.

Papa started up the motor with a tug on the cord. Mama twisted round, unable to take her eyes off our house. Up in the bow of the boat, I stared straight on, blocking out all but the steady droning of the motor. I was staring hard off at nothing when my brain registered what my eyes had been seeing. "Isn't that Granny Dell's bentwood snagged in the branches of that swamp poplar?" The old bentwood looked a strange sight rocking steadily.

"Sure seems to be. Wonder what's making it rock so?" Papa asked.

In that instant I heard it. "Meow. Meow." Just like she was yelling, "I'm here. Over here."

There was Beannie. Soaking wet and looking like the best thing I'd ever seen. Stalking back and forth across the cane seat of Granny Dell's bentwood.

Papa swung the boat into the branches of the poplar. Beannie stepped into the boat and commenced preening her wet fur and tolerating our hugs. Even from Papa. When she'd had enough fuss, she made for the carrier, curling up inside. She looked out at me, squinting like cats do. I swear she was smiling.

I know I was.

AFTER YOU READ

Find evidence

Did your predictions match with the family's decisions about what to save from their home? Note one decision made by each family member. Find evidence from the story that tells why he or she made that decision.

THE

Dust Bowl

Written by David Booth
Illustrated by Karen Reczuch

On Sunday morning, the wind blew outside the kitchen window. Matthew wiped the dust from his cereal bowl. He was used to removing the fine coating from everything in the house. It was almost as dusty inside as out. From the sideboard, the pictures of his mother and his grandma smiled at him.

When his father and his grandpa joined him at the table, they didn't say much, but he knew what they were thinking. Finally, he blurted out, "We aren't going to sell the farm, are we?"

His father set down his coffee mug and looked at Matthew's grandpa. "How much longer can we last, Pop?"

"As long as it takes," Grandpa answered.

"But the crops won't make it this year," his father snapped. "Without rain there'll be no grain. Without grain, there'll be no money."

Matthew said nothing. His grandpa stood up and walked over to the window. "The rain will come. The wheat will grow. It's not as bad as the last drought."

Matthew's father pushed his chair back angrily and went outside. He began to work in the small garden below the porch.

Matthew's grandpa sat down again, put milk and sugar in his tea, and began to talk.

"When your grandma and I first farmed this land, we were young. We thought we had discovered gold in those fields of waving wheat. The world needed wheat, and we wanted to grow enough of it for everyone.

"We plowed up all our land, even the field that we had decided not to seed yet. We borrowed from the bank and bought new equipment so we could plant as much wheat as possible. The Prairies became a one-crop country.

"We needed luck, and the first year we found it. All the farmers did. The sun shone when it was supposed to, there was enough rain, the pests stayed away, and the frost was late. Matthew, the Prairies were covered with wheat.

"How fast things change on a farm! Just the next year, in mid-June, the crops were green and growing. But by July, the heat had burned them down to nothing. When the sun took control it baked the land, and what rain there was could not soak into the ground. It was hot enough to fry your shoes. Too hot to work in the day, too hot to sleep at night. We harvested what we could, but your grandma and I began to worry.

"Then the rain stopped completely and times got worse. A hot sucking wind began to feed on the bare soil, and it blew the earth away. The grass that had fed the buffalo for centuries was no more.

"That wind blew for two solid weeks, blowing from

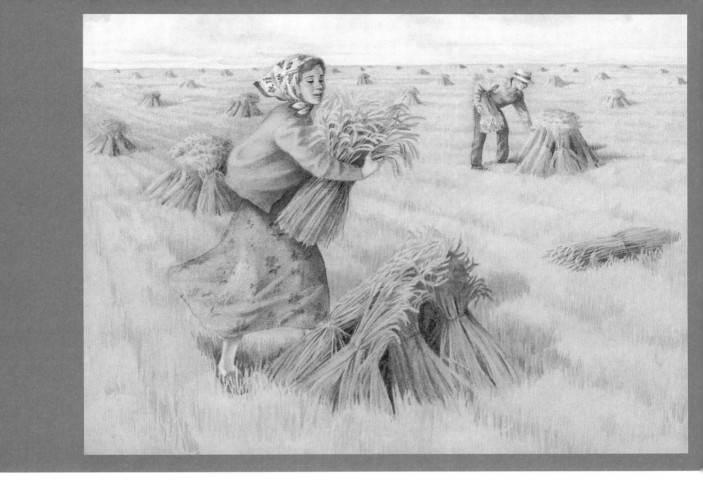

the four corners of the world, blowing the land out from
under our feet. It was the Big Dry. You had to see it to
believe it, Matthew. It turned our world into a dust bowl. It
blew open doors, broke windows, and even flattened a barn
or two.

"The dirt and the dust were everywhere. Your
grandma stuffed towels in the crack at the bottom of the
door to keep the dust out. When I went outside, I had to put
a dish towel soaked in water over my nose and mouth. The
dust drifted like snow against our fences, and even buried
them sometimes. Children had to walk to school backward
to keep the wind-blown soil from stinging their faces. And
when they got home, they had to clean the dust out of the
nostrils of the cattle.

"And, oh, the dust clouds. How I remember them. Brown ones, red ones, yellow ones, made from the soil of thousands of farms across the Prairies. One big dust cloud blocked out the sun for days. As it moved across the country it covered the land in darkness. We had to keep the lanterns lighted all day. Some people in the cities thought the end of the world had come.

"Your grandma could never get the laundry white. The curtains and the sheets were as grey as the sky. She scrubbed her fingers to the bone, but the dust kept winning. That's why we called those years the Dirty Thirties. Didn't beat your grandma, though. She fought the heat. She fought the wind. She fought the drought. Somehow she knew that she would see crops covering the fields with green again and the snow-white sheets billowing on the clothesline like great prairie schooners.

"A few of us farmers plowed deep furrows around the fields to stop the earth from blowing away. Others thought it was hopeless to keep planting because their plows just turned up dry, fine dust that blew away in the wind. A few went to church and prayed for rain. For some, farming was becoming a slow way to starve."

Through the window, Matthew saw his father beginning to weed the little garden that his mother had planted before she died.

"I'm not saying we didn't consider giving up too, but we stayed. Things got better for a time, but wouldn't you know, two years later we were hit by nature one more time.

"Another cloud covered us—grasshoppers. They could black out the sun. Millions of them would stop all at once on a farm. They ate a crop in minutes, devouring every scrap of greenness. They even ate the bristles on the broom and the halter on the horse. When a train tried to run on tracks covered with grasshoppers, the wheels could get no

traction, and they just spun around. Those insects could stop a train.

"The winter was the last straw for many farmers. It was colder than anyone could remember. We brought our mattresses into the kitchen at night to be near the heat of the cook-stove. The roads were so deep with snow that we couldn't go into town. We were cut off from everyone and everything.

"When many of my friends heard stories about the lush pickings on the west coast, they quit their farms. Tough farmers though they were, they left with their wives and kids, drained by heat and wind and cold and hardship. Chickens and everything else they owned were tied on the backs of the jalopies. Families were on the move. Schools were closed. The buildings were abandoned for good.

"Your father was born that year. We would put him on the bed between us and listen to the long whistles of the trains at night, heading west. I always loved that sound. Escape. We knew the trains were carrying farmers away from their land forever. But we couldn't leave, Matthew, we just couldn't leave. Some people's lives had dried up and blown away. But we stayed on our land and hung on to what little soil was left.

"Two years later, our land was alive again. It was green as far as the eye could see. The drought was over. The grasshoppers were gone. We were still farmers." His grandpa paused for a few moments. "That was fifty years ago, and the farm is still here. I could never have managed on my own after I lost your grandma, but your parents kept it going."

"Grandpa, is the Big Dry back?"

"I don't know, Matthew. I don't know."

They both stared out the window. The wind whistled, and swirls of dust danced across the fields.

Matthew went outside. His father put down the hoe, climbed the steps, and sat beside him on the porch. They both stared at the bluest of skies. "I love this farm, Matthew. Your mother loved it too. She was afraid to live here at first, afraid of the space and all the quiet. But when she planted her garden, she became a part of this farm. She belonged here. You do too."

Matthew took his father's hand. "Will we have to sell the farm, Dad?"

Grandpa called out through the screen door, "The rain will come. If not this year, then next year. We can hang on."

Matthew looked at his father's face and saw a smile.

"All right, Pop," his father called. "We hear you."

Matthew felt warm inside. He looked up at the sky and thought the sun winked at him. Then Matthew and his father went back into the kitchen and sat down at the table with his grandpa. The three farmers ate their cereal and waited for rain.

AFTER YOU READ

Create a time line

Look back through the story and think about the sequence of events. Create a time line to illustrate the sequence of events that happened in the story. You may choose to use sketches, diagrams, or graphics as a way to represent your time line.

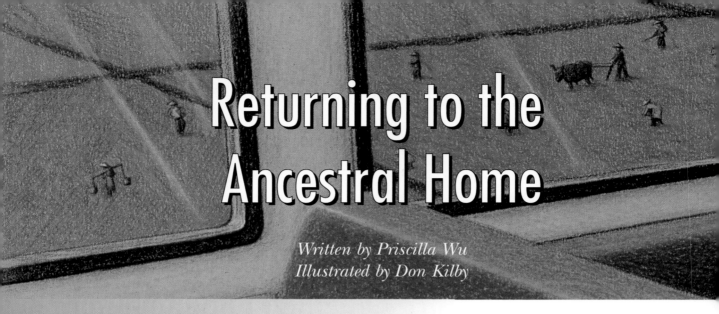

Returning to the Ancestral Home

Written by Priscilla Wu
Illustrated by Don Kilby

READING TIP

Look for word parts

When you see a word that you cannot read, look for a smaller word part in the longer word. This can help you read more difficult words. As you read, jot down any words that you find difficult to read. See if finding smaller parts in a word helps you to read it.

Mao Sheng and his father surveyed the vast checkerboard of cultivated land from the train window. Several farmers wearing bamboo hats were bent over the flooded rice fields.

"Do you remember our trip here two years ago?" His father pointed to the small, tractorlike machine chugging through the mud. "Then there were more water buffalo plowing the fields."

Mao Sheng mumbled, "Sort of." He didn't want to answer. He'd much rather be back at home warming up with his teammates for the soccer game. They needed him. After all, he was the centre forward, and today was the big playoff against Dong Shan Middle School.

"Why did I have to come?" asked Mao Sheng. "Ma Ma and Shou Mei stayed at home."

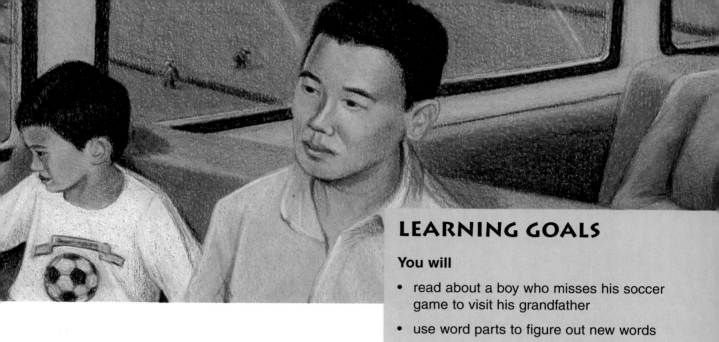

"You are Lao Da, the eldest brother," said his father. "It's an honour to come back to the ancestral home, where your grandfather was born and I was born and you were born. Besides," he continued, "we need to stay with grandfather while uncle and his family are away."

Mao Sheng looked out the window at the sugarcane leaning away from the passing train. He checked his watch. The game was about to start. In his mind's eye the referee blew the whistle and his friend Da Wei rushed for the ball after the starting kick. It should have been Mao Sheng rushing for the ball!

He sighed heavily and dozed off for a while, dreaming that he was back at school playing soccer. Unconsciously, he jumped in his sleep.

"Are you okay?" asked his father.

Half awake, Mao Sheng looked out on the rice fields and saw a miniature pagoda that housed the statue of a local harvest god.

"We're almost there," said his father.

The train slowed and Mao Sheng now saw bunches of bananas clinging, like sleeping monkeys, to the heavy, tattered trees.

"The town's so small," said Mao Sheng. "There's hardly anything here."

The whistle sounded as the train pulled into the station. Mao Sheng and his father stood up and pulled their bags from the luggage holder above them.

They left the station and began walking through town.

"There's only one real street?" asked Mao Sheng, looking down the narrow alleys on each side.

"Until a few years ago the main street was as narrow as the side streets. But it's been widened for the traffic. When I was growing up the only transportation was water buffalo and bicycle rickshas."

Mao Sheng surveyed the street vendors and began examining some videos lined up on a makeshift table.

"Grandfather lives way out in the countryside," said his father, checking his watch. "We should get there before it's dark."

Mao Sheng's father hailed a taxi and bargained with the driver until he was satisfied with the fare. Soon they were headed for the countryside.

From the back seat Mao Sheng saw the digital clock on the dashboard. By now the game was over. He was dying to know if they'd won. If only his grandfather had a phone! Then he could call one of his teammates and find out the score.

"I'm glad we moved to Chiai," said Mao Sheng.

"I am too," said his father. "But I still love coming back to the countryside."

Mao Sheng shifted in his seat. They had been travelling a long time and he was sleepy. Rousing himself, he looked out at the bright orange sunset above the rice fields. A lone scarecrow, topped with a bamboo hat, guarded the harvest.

"Aren't we going backward?" asked Mao Sheng.

"You're right," said his father. "We passed by here on the train. It won't be long now. It's just up on the left."

The sky was darkening quickly and Mao Sheng's eyes strained to see what was ahead.

"There it is!" exclaimed his father, pointing to a lighted farmhouse surrounded by a flooded rice field.

His father paid the driver, and the taxi drove away. For a moment they stood in the quiet, staring out at the crude, mud-brick dwelling overflowing with light.

"Let's go," said his father, heading for the nearest levee. Mao Sheng picked up his bag and jacket and followed his father along the middle of the narrow ridge, careful not to slip into the flooded field. Step by step, the glowing light increased in size until they stood beside it. His father pushed open the door.

"Ah Ba, Ah Ba," he said, hurrying over to a thin old man seated at a round wooden table. The old man pushed his chair back. "Don't get up," said Mao Sheng's father, putting his hand on Ah Ba's arm. Mao Sheng and his father sat down at the table, across from the oil lamp.

Mao Sheng thought Ah Ba seemed much older than he remembered him. He looked into the warm, brown eyes that glowed from the lamp's light and listened as his grandfather told them how he'd been ill, but now was feeling much better.

"Da Ge's wife fixed food before they left." Ah Ba pointed to a small cupboard. "Please, help yourself."

Mao Sheng and his father set the table with rice bowls and chopsticks and then put out the dishes of duck, dried meat, rice, and asparagus.

While eating, Mao Sheng listened to Ah Ba talk about the exceptionally good rice harvest they'd had. "We're planning to buy two more acres with our savings and the extra money from this crop." Then he turned to Mao Sheng.

"How are your grades this year?"

"He's number two in his class," said Mao Sheng's father, proudly. "And, he's the starting centre forward for the school's champion soccer team."

Mao Sheng cringed when his father's arm went around him. He was still angry about missing the game.

Ah Ba's weathered face shone, as if surrounded by a halo, through the lantern's failing light. "What a wonderful grandson you are! We are so fortunate to have you in the family."

Mao Sheng blushed. He remembered how he'd resisted visiting his grandfather.

"The lamp's very low," said Mao Sheng's father. "We should be getting ready for bed."

"You know where everything is," said Ah Ba, going slowly over to the altar of ancestor worship. He struck a match and lit a stick of incense. Mao Sheng and his father came over and stood next to him. All of them put their hands together and prayed while bowing slightly to the altar.

Mao Sheng and his father got ready for bed and then went up the ladder to the loft. Almost as soon as Mao Sheng's head touched the mattress, he fell asleep.

All of a sudden, he woke to the sound of his name being called.

"Mao Sheng! Wake Up! Hurry!" yelled his father. "Ah Ba is hurt!"

Mao Sheng sat up in the dark and looked over the edge of the loft.

"Hurry up!" yelled his father.

He quickly slid down the ladder and came over to his father. Fearfully, he looked into his grandfather's ashen face.

"He fell trying to get a drink of water, and I think his leg is broken. We'll have to take him to a doctor. Run out to the road. Flag down the first car and show him how to come down the driveway. Take the lantern over there. It has more oil. Hurry up!"

Mao Sheng lit the lantern, put on his shoes, and ran out the door. He ran frantically up the muddy driveway while praying for a car to come into view.

Mao Sheng was still tense and frightened when two bright headlights finally appeared. He swung the lantern wildly until the car pulled over to the side.

"Hurry! Come help my grandfather!" yelled Mao Sheng desperately.

He ran ahead of the car, guiding it with the lantern, until they reached the farmhouse. The man jumped from the car and ran into the house with him. He spent a few moments checking Ah Ba over and then asked Mao Sheng to bring him two pieces of firewood. "We'll need some cord or wide tape," he said. Mao Sheng found some twine in the cabinet.

The man carefully slipped the wider piece of firewood under Ah Ba's injured leg and put the other one on top of it.

He circled the leg with twine. "He'll be all right. We'll take him to the hospital so a doctor can set the leg and check him over."

"We can't thank you enough," said Mao Sheng's father.

"I'm glad he stopped me," said the young man, glancing at Mao Sheng. "You're quite a lantern-waver. If you hadn't been waving it so energetically I never would have stopped."

Flooded with pride, Mao Sheng smiled shyly. It was the same feeling he had, only much more wonderful, when people praised him for winning a soccer game. He thought about his family and how he loved belonging to it—even more than belonging to his soccer team. Then he looked down at his grandfather and realized, for the first time, that he was in the right place this weekend after all.

AFTER YOU READ

Find small parts in difficult words

Make a list of all the words that you found difficult to read. Underline or circle any smaller parts that you see in the words. Were you able to figure out how to read the words? What else could you do to figure out a word that you did not know?

What Should I Do?

In this unit, you have read about the personal choices of other people. You have learned steps to help you make wise decisions. Now it is your turn to share your decision-making skills with others by making a collection of your work.

▶ Before You Begin

Ask yourself these questions:

- Who will read my collection?
- What do I want others to know about my decision-making skills?
- How could I get feedback from my readers?
- What do I want people to notice about my work?
- How will I put my collection together?

What to Include

Your collection should include these key pieces:

- a letter to introduce yourself
- samples of your work from this unit
- a decision-making model
- an opinion piece
- a feedback piece
- your choice

Ways to Share Your Collection

- ▶ a scrapbook
- ▶ a folder
- ▶ a notebook
- ▶ a video
- ▶ a bulletin-board display

► Your First Draft

1 Introduce Yourself

- Write a letter to your readers to introduce yourself and tell what you have learned in this unit.

Here is a sample of Jennifer's letter.

> Dear reader of my collection,
> My name is Jennifer Tsoung. I live in Coquitlam, British Columbia.
> I want you to notice how my work improved. I chose two poems to show you. One I did at the beginning of the unit and one I did at the end. Please notice how I got better at making connections and expressing my feelings and ideas in my writing. I'm way better at reading too.

2 Review Your Work

- Read and revise each piece of work you have completed in this unit. Make a decision about which pieces to include.

- For each piece of work, tell the reader why you have selected it.

Simon chose to include a poem in his collection because it tells about a decision that someone else made for him.

> Decisions
>
> Leaving my China country
> Missing my favourite teacher and friends
> Leaving my school
> Leaving my house
> Go to beautiful Canada
> But to love china
>
> My parents decide
> Not me

③ Express Your Opinion

- Choose an item from a magazine, newspaper, advice column, quiz, or journal that shows someone making a decision. Include the item in your collection. Write your opinion about the item you have selected.

Jenny wrote her opinion about a question she read in a magazine quiz:

> **Remember** to use your decision-making model on page 11.

Should kids have to get A's in all their classes to play on sports teams?

> I don't think it is fair because if people like sports (which I don't) but are bad at spelling why should they quit? Where is their freedom? They could try to pull their grades higher but stile be allowed to play sports. I know education is important for your future but what about your choice?

④ Ask for Feedback

- Create a page that asks your reader for feedback about your collection and about your decision-making skills. Leave room for their responses.

Here is Moesha's feedback request sheet.

> **Feedback Sheet**
>
> When you read my work could you clearly see my decision-making model?
>
> What advice could you give me about decision-making?

What will you do with the feedback you get from readers?

▶ Put It All Together

Think about a format to use for your collection.

Matthew decided to use a scrapbook for his collection.

Try different arrangements of your pieces before gluing anything.

Revise and Edit

Go back and review what you have included in your collection.

- Ask someone else to review your work. Listen to their suggestions. Are there ways to improve?
- Proofread for errors in spelling, punctuation, and grammar.
- Check for incomplete and run-on sentences.
- Check for neat printing or writing.

Think about Your Learning

Add your own ideas about what makes a good collection.

- Is your collection neat and easily read?
- Does each piece show something you've learned about decision making?
- Have you included different forms to make it interesting for your reader?
- Is the way you put your collection together easy for others to follow?
- How will you use the feedback you get from your readers?

Unit 2: *Our Natural World*

The more we know about nature, the more we can appreciate its fragile beauty. The selections in this unit will help to inform you about how nature works in balance and what can happen when that balance is upset. As you study magazine articles, news and Internet reports, stories, and poems, you will

- explore the balance of nature and ways people can affect it
- use questions to help you investigate topics
- gather information from various sources
- report information in a variety of forms
- learn new vocabulary about topics that interest you
- write a research report

WOLF ISLAND

Written and illustrated by Celia Godkin

READING TIP

Record events

Use a chart like the one on the right to help you keep track of the events in the story. As you read, write in point form what happens in each season.

Story Beginning (First Spring)	
First Winter	
Second Spring	
Second Fall	
Second Winter	
Story End (Third Spring)	

Once there was an island. It was an island with trees and meadows, and many kinds of animals. There were mice, rabbits and deer, squirrels, foxes, and several kinds of birds.

All the animals on the island depended on the plants and other animals for their good and well-being. Some animals ate grass or other plants; some ate insects; some ate other animals. The island animals were healthy. There was plenty of food for all.

LEARNING GOALS

You will

- find out about wolves and their place in the ecosystem

- organize and summarize information in a chart

79

A family of wolves lived on the island, too, a male wolf, a female, and their five cubs. One day the wolf cubs were playing on the beach while their mother and father slept. The cubs found a strange object at the edge of the water.

It was a log raft, nailed together with boards. The cubs had never seen anything like this before. They were very curious. They climbed onto it and sniffed about. Everything smelled different.

While the cubs were poking around, the raft began to drift slowly out into the lake. At first the cubs didn't notice anything wrong. Then, suddenly, there was nothing but water all around the raft.

The cubs were scared. They howled. The mother and father wolf heard the howling and came running down to the water's edge.

They couldn't turn the raft back, and the cubs were too scared to swim, so the adult wolves swam out to the raft and climbed aboard. The raft drifted slowly and steadily over to the mainland. Finally it came to rest on the shore and the wolf family scrambled onto dry land. There were no longer wolves on the island.

Time passed. Spring grew into summer on the island, and summer into fall. The leaves turned red. Geese flew south, and squirrels stored up nuts for the winter.

Winter was mild that year, with little snow. The green plants were buried under a thin white layer. Deer dug through the snow to find food. They had enough to eat.

Next spring, many fawns were born. There were now many deer on the island. They were eating large amounts of grass and leaves. The wolf family had kept the deer population down, because wolves eat deer for food. Without wolves to hunt the deer, there were now too many deer on the island for the amount of food available.

Spring grew into summer and summer into fall. More and more deer ate more and more grass and more and more leaves.

Rabbits had less to eat, because the deer were eating their food. There were not many baby bunnies born that year. Foxes had less to eat, because there were fewer rabbits for them to hunt.

Mice had less to eat, because the deer had eaten the grass and grass seed. There were not many baby mice born that year. Owls had less to eat, because there were fewer mice for them to hunt. Many animals on the island were hungry.

The first snow fell. Squirrels curled up in their holes, wrapped their tails around them for warmth, and went to sleep. The squirrels were lucky. They had collected a store of nuts for winter.

Other animals did not have winter stores. They had to find food in the snow. Winter is a hard time for animals, but this winter was harder than most. The snow was deep and the weather cold. Most of the plants had already been eaten during the summer and fall. Those few that remained were hard to find, buried deep under the snow.

Rabbits were hungry. Foxes were hungry. Mice were hungry. Owls were hungry. Even the deer were hungry. The whole island was hungry.

The owls flew over to the mainland, looking for mice. They flew over the wolf family walking along the mainland shore. The wolves were thin and hungry, too. They had not found a home, because there were other wolf families on the mainland. The other wolves did not want to share with them.

Snow fell for many weeks. The drifts became deeper and deeper. It was harder and harder for animals to find food. Animals grew weaker, and some began to die. The deer were so hungry they gnawed bark from the trees. Trees began to die.

Snow covered the island. The weather grew colder and colder. Ice began to form in the water around the island, and along the mainland coast. It grew thicker and thicker, spreading farther and farther out into the open water. One day there was ice all the way from the mainland to the island.

The wolf family crossed the ice and returned to their old home. The wolves were hungry when they reached the island, and there were many weak and sick deer for them to eat. The wolves left the healthy deer alone.

Finally, spring came. The snow melted, and grass and leaves began to grow. The wolves remained in their island home, hunting deer. No longer would there be too many deer on the island. Grass and trees would grow again. Rabbits would find enough food. The mice would find enough food. There would be food for the foxes and owls. And there would be food for the deer. The island would have enough food for all.

Life on the island was back in balance.

AFTER YOU READ

Write a summary

Reread the story to check your chart. Make sure you have included the most important events. Use the information in your chart to write a paragraph telling the main events in the story.

Earth Cycles

Adapted from Earthcycles and Ecosystems *by Beth Savan*
Illustrated by Bart Vallecoccia and Andrew Woodhouse

We are all part of a cycle of life. This cycle goes round and round like the wheels on a bicycle. The sun starts the cycle spinning.

The Cycle of Life

1. Plants use sunlight to turn water, carbon dioxide (a gas in the air), and nutrients into leaves. This process is called *photosynthesis.* Oxygen is also released.

2. Some animals get energy by eating the plants' leaves. Other animals get energy by eating the animals that eat the leaves.

4. The soil provides food for new plants to grow.

3. People get energy by eating plants and animals. Both animals and people breathe in oxygen produced by photosynthesis. When plants and animals die, their bodies rot and enrich the soil.

Food Chains

All animals can be divided into groups based on what they eat:

- *Carnivores* eat meat (other animals).
- *Herbivores* eat plants and eat no meat.
- *Omnivores* (such as most humans) eat a bit of everything.
- *Decomposers* (such as cockroaches and worms) are nature's garbage cans. They eat any animal or vegetable material that's left over from other animals' needs.

Put these groups all together and they form a kind of living food chain. Food chains link the flow of energy from one living thing to another. Because no other animals eat wolves, wolves are at the top of their food chain. Humans are also at the top of their food chain. Food chains link nature's communities together.

Ecosystems and Natural Balance

An ecosystem is like a huge creature that eats, drinks, and breathes. Ecosystems consist of animals and plants and the air, water, and earth they need to survive—all working together. No part can survive without the others, just as your hand couldn't live if it was separated from the rest of your body.

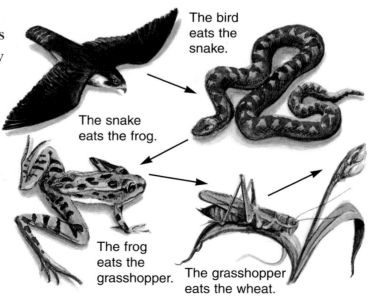

The bird eats the snake.

The snake eats the frog.

The frog eats the grasshopper.

The grasshopper eats the wheat.

Sometimes an ecosystem goes out of balance, putting the survival of plants and animals—and, eventually, people—at risk. The causes may be natural, such as changes in weather, fires, or flooding. We humans and our buildings and factories may disturb an ecosystem. People are great at taking from the natural world, and often not so great at giving back to it. But there are many things people are doing to help bring back the natural balance.

AFTER YOU READ

Illustrate a cycle

What other events occur in a cycle? Here are some ideas: days, the calendar year, sports seasons, fashions. Choose another event and illustrate it in a cycle.

The
Endless March

Written by Bramwell Ryan
From Equinox *magazine*

READING TIP

Use headings to predict

Many writers use text organizers, such as headings and
subheadings, to organize their information. Scan the
headings. What do you think each section will be about?

On the Move

Serge Couturier is waiting for
the caribou to swim. The
George River caribou, that is.
Why? These caribou are special
for at least two important
reasons. First, there are lots of
George River caribou at the
moment—about 800 000.
Secondly, this herd of caribou
migrates up to 9000 km a year
in search of food. It travels the
Ungava Peninsula, across
northern Quebec and
Labrador. The George River
caribou migration is the last
great migration on land in
North America.

Couturier is one of only
four scientists studying the
movement of these animals and
he is a hands-on kind of guy.
Several times a year, in all
seasons, this wildlife biologist
travels north. He tracks, counts,
and photographs George River
caribou.

He also captures them. The
easiest way to do that is while
they are swimming.

Taking the Plunge

The cry goes up. Thousands of
caribou have swept southeast
along the shore of Ungava Bay.
They had reached the broad

mouth of the huge Koksoak River. Then they headed south along the river, looking for a narrow spot to cross. Near the tiny village of Kuujjuaq they have found that spot.

That is where Couturier waits. He has learned that the caribou have air sacs inside their skin. So they float like corks. They are easy to spot, swimming high on the waves.

Couturier and his crew head out in a rubber Zodiac. The river is so cold it burns. Couturier knows this first hand. It is his arm that plunges into the freezing river and captures a calf in a headlock. Couturier hauls the 60-kg animal, kicking and flailing, into the unsteady boat.

Measurements of the caribou's chest and foreleg are taken. A bright red tag is stapled to its ear. An expandable leather satellite collar is fastened around its neck. Finally, the animal is weighed. Then on to the next caribou.

Meet the George River Caribou

One hundred and two distinct breeds of caribou exist in North America but only eight have populations over 100 000. None travel as far as the George River caribou. And no caribou living in the southern portion of the peninsula face the same survival threats as the George River caribou, that is, too many mouths to feed on too little food.

The George River caribou are a mixture of blond, brown, and grey. Their shoulders come up to about midchest height on a human, about one metre. As they walk, they click. A small tendon in the heel of their hind legs slipping across the bone makes this characteristic sound. Couturier believes that the clicking sounds help the herd stay together during a blinding snowstorm.

Every spring, the female caribou return to their calving ground. Here they give birth to a single calf each. By four days of age, the calves can outrun wolves.

Soon, the herd of females and calves masses together. The caribou head toward the southwest. They rejoin the males near the Caniapiscau River. Now the whole herd travels old migratory routes across the vast Quebec-Labrador Peninsula. The George River caribou search for greenery, willow and birch leaves, and grass.

In the autumn, males with mighty antlers battle for mates. When the short mating season is over, their rack of antlers falls off. Female caribou have antlers too, but their headgear does not fall off. It remains throughout the winter.

Then There Were Few

Couturier is taking a risk to study the unique George River caribou. Why? One of the reasons is the changing population of the herd.

There are lots of them, right? Well, at the moment there are. And in 1890 there were, too. But in the early 1900s, the George River caribou almost disappeared.

This was a problem for the local Inuit people. The survival of the Inuit rose and fell according to the size of the caribou herd. Daisy Watt is a

Migration Area of the George River Caribou

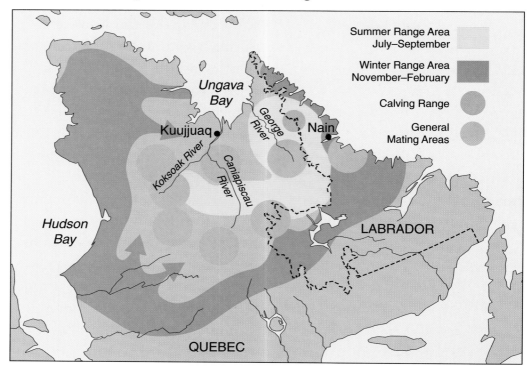

76-year-old Inuit elder living in Kuujjuaq. She explains that when she was born, in 1922, there were no caribou at all. "My grandparents told me there used to be lots. They disappeared. Many people starved, and the hunters had to go so far to find the caribou. Some never came back."

In the middle of the 1900s, the George River caribou became so rare that biologists suggested capturing a few. They believed caring for them in a zoo would at least make sure the breed would survive!

But starting in 1970, the population began to grow wildly. The population of the George River caribou herd rises and falls in cycles. No one knows why. That's where Couturier comes into the picture.

Trying to Solve the Mystery

Couturier believes that the George River caribou's population explosion has come to a halt. The population is beginning to decline again. And Couturier is trying to find out why.

Some people blame humans. In Labrador, military jets fly about 6000 training flights every year. The jets fly up to 800 km an hour at heights as low as 35 m from the ground. Some people believe the noise is disturbing the caribou and hurting their populations. Fred Harrington, an ecologist in Halifax, says they aren't really a problem. He studies the effects of low-level flights on a herd of caribou near Goose Bay.

Some people believe hydroelectric dams are at fault. They flood vast areas of wilderness to create reservoirs. Couturier agrees that flooding has taken away some of the caribou's land. But he says, "The impact on animals is minimal."

Couturier predicts that there will be 200 000 caribou alive in 15 years. That will be 600 000 fewer than there are today. It's still lots of caribou, but Couturier doesn't think they will almost disappear. He believes that the decline will be a natural event, part of a natural cycle. The mystery goes on. The studies continue.

A Strange Feeling

It seems that the success of the George River caribou is its greatest threat. The more there are, the more mouths there are to feed. The more mouths, the less food to go around. The caribou must travel farther and burn more energy. This lowers their birth rate.

Couturier continues to think about the mystery and marvel at these animals. "They are amazing," he says. "I still get a strange feeling when I see them. They're free, and I hope there are never so few that I can count them all."

AFTER YOU READ

Make notes using headings

Reread the selection and make notes about the main ideas or events under each heading. Write down one way that the headings helped you read and understand the selection.

Internet News Update

November 18, 1996

No Rescue for Peary Caribou

Severe weather delayed a recent Peary caribou rescue effort. The rescue can't be attempted again until next fall. In the meantime, the 2000 remaining Peary caribou are dealing with their third harsh winter in a row.

The rescue mission left Winnipeg on November 1. It stopped in Edmonton to pick up more members, then set up camp at Resolute Bay. But on Saturday, November 2, the first day of the caribou rescue, the team was forced to turn back.

Freezing rain, wet snow, and high winds caused dangerous whiteout conditions. By the time the weather cleared, there were only two hours of light left each day.

The rescuers must wait until next fall to make another attempt. During the spring and short Arctic summer, the caribou are not healthy and strong enough to be moved safely.

—from *ALBERTA REPORT, The Weekly Newsmagazine—Internet edition*

LEARNING GOALS

You will

- find out about a rescue team that tried to save a special breed of endangered caribou in the Arctic

- learn how to find the key ideas in a news report

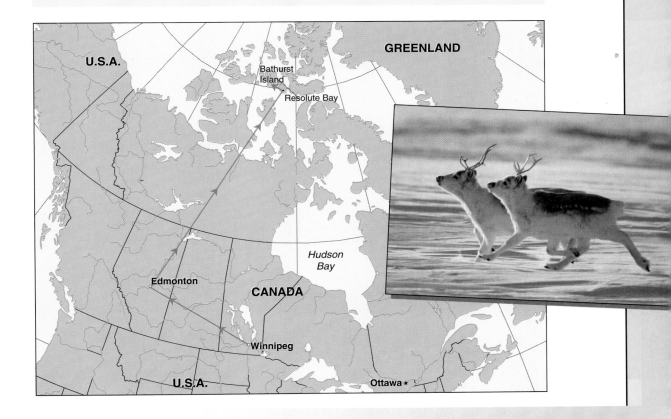

AFTER YOU READ

Summarize

News reports answer the questions Who? What? When? Where? Why? and How? Use these "5 Ws + H" as headings to create a chart in your notebook. Use the chart to summarize the information in this article.

Key Ideas
Who?
What?
When?
Where?
Why?
How?

Survival in the City

Written by Diane Swanson
Illustrated by Bart Vallecoccia

READING TIP

Find main ideas

Many nonfiction selections are organized by topic, main ideas, and details:

- topic—what a selection is about
- main ideas—what each section or paragraph is about
- details—more information about a main idea

As you read, think about the main idea of each section.

At Home in the City

There are coyotes in the crosswalk and frogs in the swimming pool ... skunks waddling through churchyards and falcons diving off skyscrapers. With all its many buildings, streets, and parks, the city may be home to people, but it is also home to wildlife.

Having wildlife in the city is not something new. Pigeons nested on houses and temples more than 6000 years ago. What's new is the study of the wildlife that lives in the city. It was the 1960s before scientists saw the city as a unique ecosystem—a place where living things affect each other and their surroundings in a special way. Now we are just beginning to learn how animals, including people, live together in the city.

City Life

The city provides many kinds of homes where animals can nest, rest, escape harsh weather, and hide from their enemies. Bridges, billboards, and buildings—from sheds to high-rises—are some of the things animals perch on, snuggle in, or burrow under. Many parks, golf courses, schoolyards, cemeteries, and

97

Critter Crossing

Spring-fed ponds and plenty of food were attracting herons, ducks, otters, and raccoons to a neighbourhood in Saanich, British Columbia. But cars were hitting slow-moving ducklings and young raccoons as they crossed a busy road. One woman in the neighbourhood painted up some special crossing signs. Then she posted them on the street to warn drivers to watch for animals.

neighbourhoods offer small "forests" of trees and shrubs. Backyards provide hideaways in rockeries, compost boxes, and stacks of firewood.

When animals move into the city—or rove within it—they need safe places to travel and rest. They may follow railway tracks or move among bushes and trees that line roads or divide highway lanes. Once in town, some animals travel secretly through underground pipes connecting neighbourhoods. Some cities also have subway tunnels or wooded ravines that animals follow.

There is an almost endless supply of water and food in the city. Lakes in parks, ponds in yards, and sprinklers on lawns are some of the places animals drink. And gardens, garbage, and grocery stores provide plenty of food. Many city animals also prey on other city animals, like insects and mice. They don't have to compete for food and water with as many different animals as they would in the country. City animals don't have to travel as far to get food, either.

Despite the traffic, which kills lots of wildlife, city animals face fewer dangers than their country cousins. Hunting and shooting are not allowed in cities. People use smaller amounts of pesticides in cities than they do at many farms and orchards. And some of the animals who move to cities leave behind many of the country animals who eat them.

Cities also differ in climate. Their buildings block winds that sweep across the country. But some streets channel the wind, causing "wind tunnels," and tall buildings often cause updrafts.

Most cities are warmer than the country, both day and night. Buildings and roads hold the heat that comes from the sun, and traffic, machinery, and factories create more heat. At night, cities release heat more slowly than the countryside does.

The Starling Is Ringing

Some birds make loud noises to scare their enemies. The starling, a songbird that lives in most cities in Canada, often imitates the calls of bigger birds. It also copies the barking of dogs and the meowing of cats. Even more startling are the sounds it imitates on city streets: the shrieking of car burglar alarms and the ringing of portable telephones.

The warm air often makes city skies cloudier—and that leads to more rain and snow. At least five to ten per cent more moisture normally falls in the city than in the country. Because of the city's warmer climate, some animals, like pigeons, reproduce throughout the year. Cities may even attract other animals, like opossums, that usually live farther south.

City Types

City life isn't for everyone. Wolves are one kind of wildlife that prefers places far from traffic lights and shopping malls. Other animals, like bears and cougars, often just pass through cities or wander in and out, looking for food.

Still others adapt well, have their young and spend all, or much, of their lives in the city.

Last Minute Mice

Travellers waiting for subway trains in Toronto, Ontario, can spot lots of mice. The animals scurry along dark track lines, nibbling crumbs of food. But they know when to take a break. As the train speeds into the station, they scamper off the track. Just in time, they duck into nooks and crannies on either side or dive under the rails themselves. As soon as the train pulls out, these city-wise mice are back, rummaging for food again.

They are usually animals that are smaller than large dogs and can find enough space in the city. They are also animals not easily frightened by strange noises or objects. And many of them are most active at night when cities are least busy.

Above all, city animals are flexible. Most eat many types of foods: plants and animals—living or dead. They are also willing to try new foods, like watermelon and pizza. They feed on things that are easy to find in cities. Birds, for instance, feast on insects that are attracted to street lights.

City animals accept different—often unnatural—homes. Bats rest in attics and church spires instead of hollow trees and caves. Magpies make nests in construction cranes; chimney swifts, in chimneys.

One of the most successful city animals is the house sparrow. It never seems to mind the hustle and bustle of the city and it eats many different foods. It nests anywhere from signs to drainpipes, and often builds its nest with lots of "city stuff," like string, paper, plastic, and rags.

Scientists think that animals that live in the city will become even better at it in 50 to 100 years. And some think that people should learn to adapt to the animals. That's not easy when raccoons raid the garden and skunks dig holes in the lawn. But as scientists learn more about city ecosystems, they may find ways to help people and animals live together with less trouble.

Main Ideas	Details
1.	•
	•
	•
2.	•
	•

AFTER YOU READ

Summarize content

A summary of main ideas and details can help you remember the information in a selection. Beside the headings "Main Ideas" and "Details," summarize the section "City Types."

For the Birds

Written by Susan Hughes

READING TIP

Ask questions

What questions would you like to ask someone who cares for injured birds? Write down 3–5 questions you would like answered. Leave spaces for the answers. As you read this interview, look for answers to your questions.

VANCOUVER ISLAND, BRITISH COLUMBIA

Sylvia Campbell and her husband, Robin, run the North Island Wildlife Recovery Association on Vancouver Island, British Columbia. They care for wild birds and other animals that are ill, injured, and orphaned. Many school children visit Sylvia and Robin to see and learn about these wild creatures.

SUSAN: What kinds of birds are brought to you?

SYLVIA: We see many bald eagles and golden eagles, owls, hawks, crows, songbirds, herons, and turkey vultures.

SUSAN: How are eagles injured?

SYLVIA: Some have gunshot wounds or lead shot poisoning. Others have been electrocuted by power lines or are starving.

SUSAN: How do you care for the eagles?

Robin Campbell cares for two owls at the North Island Wildlife Recovery Association, Vancouver Island, B.C.

SYLVIA: We have a large flight cage that is 43 m long, 9 m wide, and 6 m high. It can house up to 20 eagles. The eagles practise flying in this cage after their injuries have healed. Their wings become strong again. Then we release them into the wild.

SUSAN: How long do birds usually stay with you?

SYLVIA: We try to release the birds as soon as their injuries are healed. A bird with a minor injury might be released after two weeks. A more serious injury could mean a bird is with us for as long as nine months. There are some birds we can never release. We have two turkey vultures, for example, whose wings were shattered by gunshot. They never fully recovered. They are poor flyers now, so they can't be released.

SUSAN: Tell me more about the turkey vultures.

SYLVIA: Ichabod is the friendliest. He sits on our arm and lets people have a really close look at him. He helps us teach children the difference between raptors, which prey on live animals, and scavengers, like Ichabod, which feed on dead animals. Ichabod is actually a television star, too! He appeared on an episode of the TV series *The X-Files*.

TORONTO, ONTARIO

Lori Nichols is a volunteer member of the Fatal Light Awareness Program (FLAP). Many songbirds fly through downtown Toronto, Ontario, at night, especially when they are migrating. The lights on tall city buildings attract and confuse these birds. Many birds fly into the windows.

FLAP volunteer Lori Nichols examines an injured bird in downtown Toronto, ON.

SUSAN: How do FLAP volunteers rescue birds?

LORI: Between four and five in the morning, volunteers head for the tallest city towers with lights on. They search for birds beneath the buildings until just after dawn. They find mostly songbirds, such as ovenbirds and white-throated sparrows. Some are dead. Some are injured or just stunned. The volunteers put the live birds in brown paper bags. Some days there may be only two or three birds. On our busiest days, we collect over 200 live birds.

SUSAN: How do you help, Lori?

LORI: If 15 or more birds are collected, I drive downtown and examine them. I treat the birds with head injuries. Then I take them to the Toronto Wildlife Centre or the Toronto Humane Society. Or I take them home. I hand feed the birds every two hours. Broken bones are too tiny for me to set. I let the birds rest and heal on their own. Then I let them go.

SUSAN: What do you do with birds that are stunned but uninjured?

LORI: I put a band on their legs. Then I drive out of the city and release them. If it's fall and the birds are going south, I release them west of the city. We hope they follow the shoreline west and then south. We hope they won't be attracted back to Toronto by the city lights.

SUSAN: Why are you involved in FLAP?

LORI: I am a birdwatcher. After hearing about FLAP, I went downtown one night. The lights were on at the CN Tower. I could see—and *hear*—the birds flying into the windows and falling. This convinced me that I had to help. The CN Tower now turns off its night lights. This has made an amazing difference to the birds. FLAP is working to get the lights on the other tall buildings turned off, too!

A biologist from the Long Point Bird Observatory in Ontario bands a bird to track its migration patterns.

GANDER, NEWFOUNDLAND

Heather Tonner cares for wild birds and animals in the backyard and basement of her home in Gander, Newfoundland. Sometimes she looks after as many as 10 to 12 birds at one time.

SUSAN: What kinds of birds are brought to you?

HEATHER: I get mainly robins. I have birds injured by cat bites. But 90 per cent of them aren't injured. They are human-made orphans.

SUSAN: Can you explain this?

HEATHER: Baby birds live in the nest until they are 10 to 14 days old. Then they move out to the branches. These "branchers" can't fly yet. A lot of the birds that are brought to me are branchers that have fallen out of a tree. This is part of the learning process for the birds. The parents will still feed them on the ground. But people find them and think that because these birds can't fly, this means they are injured.

SUSAN: How do you care for the orphans?

HEATHER: I have them for about two to three weeks. I feed the baby robins every two hours on a special diet. I keep them indoors until they can fly. Then I move them to my outdoor flight cage.

SUSAN: What happens then?

HEATHER: I fill a pan with compost and I put it in the flight cage. The robins learn to hunt in the soil for insects. When they can feed themselves this way, it is time to get them used to being outside again. So I release them into my backyard during the day for two or three days. They don't go far—and they wait for me to feed them. But I bring them back inside at night. Eventually they become more wild and more cautious.

Heather Tonner feeds orphaned robins on her porch in Gander, Nfld.

SUSAN: Is that when you stop feeding them?

HEATHER: Yes. I stop feeding them and begin leaving them out all the time. Sometimes they will sit at the patio door and chirp for food. It breaks my heart not to feed them. But two or three days after that, they're off. And that is what makes me happy. I do what I do for the love of these birds.

AFTER YOU READ

Find answers

Look back through the interview for answers to the questions you wrote down before reading. Write down any information that helps to answer your questions. If there is no information about one of your questions, try to think of at least two places you could find the answer.

An Interview on the Internet

Written by Denzil Reid and the Students of Burgoyne's Cove Elementary School, Newfoundland

Denzil Reid is a school principal in Newfoundland. He has two Newfoundland ponies that recently produced a colt. Students in Burgoyne's Cove Elementary School decided to interview Mr. Reid in cyberspace.

Q: How many ponies do you have?

A: We have two ponies right now.

Q: How old are your ponies?

A: My ponies are quite young. Our mare, Lady, is seven, and Star, the stallion, will soon be eight. Ponies can live for more than 30 years.

Q: Have your ponies ever had babies?

A: Yes. Lady had a colt last October. We called him Sebastian. He was really beautiful and grew very fast. In February he went to his new home. He is doing well.

Q: What do your Newfoundland ponies look like?

A: Newfoundland ponies come in several colours and mixtures of colours. They come in three sizes too. Both of our ponies are brown with white star patches on their foreheads. Star has one white hoof. Both ponies are very gentle and love kids. That's typical of the breed. Over many thousands of years they have adapted to cold weather. Legs, ears, and noses have grown closer to the body. Short legs and ears and flattened faces are three main characteristics. As added protection, their ears are thickly covered with hair—even on the inside. They can move their ears like a satellite dish in the direction of a sound. They hear better than we do.

Q: What do your ponies eat?

A: The ponies eat hay. Lots and lots of hay. This winter we have used more than 300 bales. A bale contains about 20 kg. In addition to hay, they eat corn, barley, and oats. They love apples and pears. Vegetable peelings, stale bread, and crackers are also popular. For a special treat, we sometimes give them sugar cubes.

Q: Do your ponies have funny ears?

A: The ponies have small ears.

Q: Where do Newfoundland ponies live?

A: Newfoundland ponies live all over the island but in very small numbers. Right now there are around only 100 ponies left, which means the species is in danger of becoming extinct. When I was a boy, there were more than 100 just on the little island where I lived, and more than 6000 on the main island of Newfoundland. Today, Lady and Star are the only ponies in my town.

Q: Why is the Newfoundland pony endangered?

A: Why so few when once there were so many? They are no longer needed for working in the woods and around the communities the way they were in the past. Machines have now taken over their work. In addition, the pony is no longer allowed to wander around the island. Few people can afford enough fenced property to keep even one pony. Remember how much food they eat.

Q: Can Newfoundland ponies die if the weather is too cold?

A: These ponies can stand very cold weather. It is one of their special features. We leave the barn door open so that they can come and go as they like. Even in the very cold they seem to prefer the shelter of a thick clump of trees to their barn. They have an undercoat and a very thick outercoat that gives them added protection. Their winter coat can be as much as 10 cm longer than their summer coat. They really know how to protect themselves from wind, rain, or snow. I think they are amazing.

Q: Do you have to own a Newfoundland pony to join the Newfoundland Pony Society?

A: You do not. It might be a good idea for your class to take out a membership. You will receive their newsletter, which contains a lot of interesting information. Happy studies. My ponies and I thank you.

Interesting Newfoundland Pony Facts

EYES

- Newfoundland ponies can see behind and to both sides at the same time!

  (This helped protect the ponies from predators when they lived in Asia and Europe.)

- Newfoundland ponies can't see clearly things in front and up close!

  (If you offer a pony a treat, it will tilt its head up to get a better look.)

SIZE

- Horses and ponies are measured in a unit called a *hand*.
  (1 hand = 11 cm)

- Standard-sized Newfoundland ponies are 12–13 hands high and weigh 340 kg.

DEADLY FOODS

- Too many yew bushes or acorns will kill a Newfoundland pony!

AFTER YOU READ

Reread for information

Add new information to your chart. Reread the story to make sure you've included all of the important information. Do you want to change any information that you recorded before you read the story?

NEWFOUNDLAND PONIES:
A Memoir

Written by Linda Doody
Illustrated by Angela Vaculik

Linda Doody grew up with Newfoundland ponies nearby. She writes about her childhood memories and love for Newfoundland ponies.

READING TIP

Create "mind pictures" as you read

As you read about the author's memories, try to picture the scenes she describes. Note the words and details she uses to make you feel as if you were watching.

I grew up in a small Newfoundland community that was a happy blend of yesterdays and todays. Noisy airplanes from the nearby naval base shared the skies with quiet gulls. Roaring trains sped by forests where ponies roamed and goats grazed. It seemed long-haired, short-legged Newfoundland ponies were everywhere, grazing in the fields or pulling wooden carts or sleighs along the road. I was lucky—the ponies were a part of my everyday life.

Nellie

One of my best early memories is of Nellie. She was a gentle white Newfoundland pony. Nellie belonged to our neighbour. Each morning he would hitch her to a small, wooden cart and collect and deliver mail for the people living on our country road. My brothers and I would run out to meet the postal cart—with a detour through Mother's flower garden. We were treated to a short ride in the back of the cart until we reached our gate. We always had words of thanks for our friendly mail carrier, and special treats for Nellie. Her favourite food was fresh carrots—leaves and all. Other ponies roamed wild in the woods near our house. They were gentle, friendly creatures with short, sure-footed legs and shaggy coats, but Nellie was extra-special to me. She was a regular visitor, she had her own name, and she tossed her head gratefully when I fed her treats.

Jip

We often visited an uncle who lived on another part of the island. Uncle had a Newfoundland pony called Jip. All of our island ponies were determined, but Jip was stubborn. So was my uncle. One frosty winter day, they decided to match wits. Uncle hitched Jip to a sturdy sleigh that was

loaded with freshly cut firewood. He jumped into his seat, tugged the reins, and shouted for Jip to pull. Jip did not feel like pulling. The coaxing went on for some time. Then, at the moment my uncle least expected it, Jip decided to cooperate. Jip bolted forward, the sleigh lurched, and Uncle tumbled off his perch and rolled down the ice-glazed hill. I know now that ponies don't smile; I knew then that Uncle didn't. I covered my smile with my thick woollen scarf and muffled a giggle.

Coco

As I grew from child to teen to adult, I almost forgot Nellie, Jip, and those short shaggy visitors to our woods. The birth of our daughter, Lesley, brought back my dreams and memories of childhood. Lesley was like me—she loved ponies. But her ponies were in books and on television. There were no daily cart rides and backyard visits, as there had been when I was a child. Newfoundland ponies no longer roamed freely through our island's fields. Cars had the road to themselves. Something was missing!

When Lesley was old enough, we began to drive the 130 km from our town to a stable near St. John's. There she took riding lessons and became good friends with her favourite animals. Of all the horses in the stable, Coco was her favourite. Coco was a chocolate-coloured, shaggy-haired pony with a dark mane and tail—a true Newfoundland pony. As I watched Lesley bouncing along on Coco's strong back, I began to wonder what had happened to the ponies that had shared my childhood. I soon found out the answer.

Lady, Star, and Sebastian

I met with Denzil Reid, a principal of a school about three-and-a-half hours from our home. He had three Newfoundland ponies and invited my family and me to visit. We were thrilled. Lesley became good friends with Lady, Star, and their foal, Sebastian.

I learned from Denzil that the Newfoundland ponies were endangered. He and other people around the province were determined not to let them become extinct. Denzil gave me three books to read by Dr. Andrew Fraser, a retired veterinarian with a deep respect for the threatened pony. Dr. Fraser helped found the Newfoundland Pony Society.

Their efforts gave me hope for Newfoundland ponies. I began to work with people like Denzil and Dr. Fraser. Thanks to people who care, I hope that Lesley and her children and their children will always have friendly Nellies and stubborn, clever Jips in their lives.

AFTER YOU READ

Sketch and make a word web

Pick out a scene in the selection that is especially clear in your mind. Sketch the scene as you see it in your "mind's eye." Record some of the author's words and phrases around your sketch.

Watching Grey
WHALES

Written by J. S. Baird

READING TIP

Create "mind pictures"

As you read this poem, try to picture the whales in your mind. Notice the words that the poet uses to create a picture for you.

LEARNING GOALS

You will

- read a poet's word pictures about grey whales

- respond personally to a poem

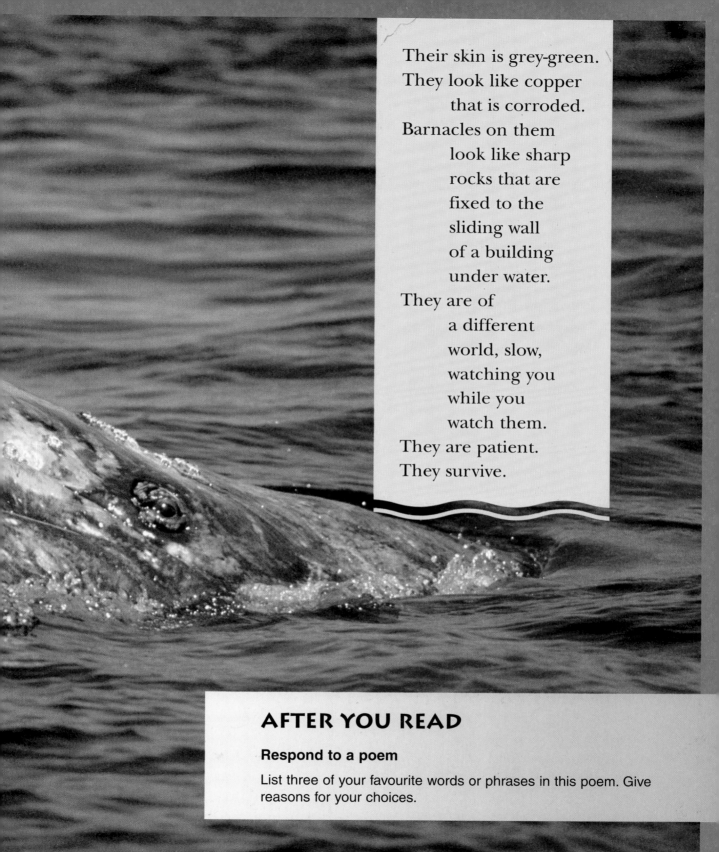

Their skin is grey-green.
They look like copper
    that is corroded.
Barnacles on them
    look like sharp
    rocks that are
    fixed to the
    sliding wall
    of a building
    under water.
They are of
    a different
    world, slow,
    watching you
    while you
    watch them.
They are patient.
They survive.

AFTER YOU READ

Respond to a poem

List three of your favourite words or phrases in this poem. Give
reasons for your choices.

The STORY of THREE WHALES

Written by Giles Whittell
Illustrated by Scott Cameron

READING TIP

Track story events

This selection is a narrative (a story about "what happened").
As with many stories, it is based on a problem and attempts
to find a solution. As you read, keep track of the events with
a chart like the one below.

Problem	Solution
Whales were trapped in ice	lst try:
	2nd try:

For twelve bright weeks every summer, the Arctic Ocean is
full of life. Blooms of plankton float among the icebergs.
Shellfish slide along the sea floor. Squid lurk under pitch-
black overhangs of rock. And whales swim up from the
Pacific to feed.

Humpback whales, Bowhead whales, and California Gray whales all come to the Arctic. In the summer of 1988 one particular herd of California Grays was plunging and rolling, leaping and belly-flopping, off the north coast of Alaska.

LEARNING GOALS

You will

- learn the true story of three Gray whales that were trapped under the Arctic ice and the people who helped them

- use a chart to keep track of what happens in a story

But winter came early in 1988. The first sign was a freezing wind from the east. Blizzards blew in from the top of the world. Thick pack ice spread out from the shore and its shadow fell over the whales.

Most of the whales were quick to sense the changes. In small groups, they set off on the long swim south to warmth for the winter. But three of the whales failed to notice the end of summer—one adult, one middle-sized, one baby.

Quietly the ice crept in. The ocean was changing from blue to silent white. Gray whales can hold their breath under water for half an hour, but soon the three who had been left behind would have nowhere left to surface.

Only the open water was safe, beyond the pack ice. But the three whales lost their sense of direction. They swam

toward land, into an Alaskan bay, where the still, shallow water was certain to freeze very quickly.

At the mouth of the bay was a shelf of ice, under water. Broken pack ice piled up against it, forming a wall. From seabed to surface there was no way out.

Then the surface froze solid. The whales were trapped in a prison of ice. They could not breathe. Again and again they rammed upward at the ice with their noses.

At last they managed to push their great heads through a crack in the ice. An Inuit hunter was passing and saw them. In nearby Barrow, an Inuit town, he told people what he had seen.

To begin with, nothing was done to save the whales. It would be natural for the whales to die and the Inuit accepted it. But the news of the whales began to spread. Their pictures appeared on local TV.

One person who heard the news was a wildlife ranger. She persuaded the people of Barrow to help keep the whales alive. Out over the ice they trudged, with axes, ice poles, and chainsaws to cut breathing holes.

The whales appeared at the holes and filled their huge lungs. The Inuit gave them names: Siku (the biggest), Poutu (the middle one), and Kannick (the baby). *Siku* means ice in Inuit. *Poutu* means ice hole, and *Kannick* means snowflake.

The Inuit cut a line of breathing holes, out toward the open water. They worked for fourteen days and nights. Clattering chainsaws sliced constantly through the ice, but the water would quickly freeze solid again.

Siku, Poutu, and Kannick refused to follow the line of holes. They stayed by the shore where they knew they could breathe. "The Plight of the Whales" became front-page news all over the world. Millions of people waited in hope.

From all across America, offers of help poured in. But nothing could break through the wall of ice at the mouth of the bay. An enormous bulldozer tried, but stuck fast.

A sky-crane helicopter hammered the ice with a concrete torpedo. It punched a line of holes from the whales to the wall. But still the whales wouldn't follow.

Their noses were bloody and scraped to the bone. The ice was invincible. It seemed to the watching world that the whales must die. Polar bears stalked the ice, waiting patiently for a feast of whale meat.

One evening Siku and Poutu surfaced alone. Being the smallest, Kannick was also the weakest. Morning came and still only Siku and Poutu appeared at the hole. No one could say exactly what had happened. And no one ever saw Kannick again.

On the twentieth day, Siku and Poutu felt the tremble of distant engines. A huge Russian icebreaker was roaring to the rescue, the great *Admiral Makarov*.

The captain found a grand phrase to mark the occasion. "Let us begin to break ice!" he called. All night the breaker charged at the ice, pulled back, and charged again.

By morning a channel was clear, half a kilometre wide. The crew of the *Admiral Makarov* grinned. They came ashore to celebrate and the Inuit and other Americans hugged them and cheered.

124

Then the icebreaker turned for the open sea with Siku and Poutu close behind. The whales understood that they must follow the thunder and froth of the engines. The sound would lead them from the prison of ice, to the open water and freedom.

The rest of the herd was three weeks ahead on the journey south. Siku and Poutu had thousands of kilometres to swim. So they each blew a great waterspout and set off.

Their long ordeal was over now.

AFTER YOU READ

Retell the story

Use the information you recorded in your chart to help you retell the story as a newscast for a newspaper, radio, or television. Don't forget to give the most important information in the first sentence, and tell about the "5Ws + H" (Who? What? When? Where? Why? and How?).

Our Natural World

In this unit, you have learned how animals live in different environments. You have read stories, magazine and Internet articles, interviews, and a poem to gather information about different topics. Now it's your turn to use what you have learned to write a research report.

▶ Before You Begin

Choose an animal in the natural world which interests you. Ask yourself these questions:

- Who will read my research report?
- What do I already know about my animal?
- What questions do I have?
- What research resources will I use?

Research Tip

Animal research questions are often organized using these categories:

- food
- habitat
- appearance
- enemies
- interesting facts

Rajiv decided to do his report on hawks. He used a chart like this to organize his thinking.

What I already know	What I need to find out
• Hawks build nests.	• Where do they build their nests?
• Hawks hunt for their food.	• What do hawks eat?

▶ Gather Your Information

1 Write each question on a separate piece of paper. Keep your question to the left side of the page. You'll need room for more columns later.

What does	
a hawk eat?	

3 different resources

Bye!

Research Resources

- books
- encyclopedias
- magazines
- newspapers
- videos
- CD-ROMs
- the Internet

2 Learn more about you... least three sources.

3 Identify your three sou... next to the question. N... column for each sourc...

4 As you collect information from each source, record what you find out. Work with one question at a time. Use point form.

Hawks	Encyclopedia	Book	Interview
	World Book	Hawks	Neighbour
Where do hawks build their nests?	in trees, on cliffs	on the ground (in places with no trees)	in satellite dish (include photo)

> **Remember,** people are resources too. Don't forget to ask friends, family, and neighbours who know about your topic. Ask if you can interview them.

▶ Write Your First Draft

1 **Write the beginning.**

- Your first paragraph should tell what your report is about.
- You can also tell your readers an interesting fact about your animal to get their interest.

Here's how Rajiv began his report. He used humour to hook his readers.

> If you are afraid of heights, you wouldn't make a very good hawk!

2 **Write the main section of your report.**

- This is where you include answers to the questions you researched.
- Put the answers to each question in a separate paragraph.

Rajiv started the main section of his report like this.

> Most hawks build their nests high up in the top of a tree. They spend most of their awake time soaring through the clouds, looking for food to catch.

3 **Write your ending.**

- End with an important idea. You might tell what you have learned or how you feel.

Rajiv ended his report by telling how he feels about his subject.

> Hawks are graceful but powerful creatures. I'm glad I got the chance to see one in the air.

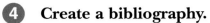

4 **Create a bibliography.**

- List the sources of information you used in your report.
- Use headings to separate book sources, magazine sources, and so on.
- Arrange items alphabetically by author's last name or book title.
- Underline book titles. Put titles of magazine articles in quotation marks.
- Give the publisher and date of publication.

> ▶ Put It All Together

What will you include in your report?

Photos

Headings

Diagrams

Charts

| Books |
| Duncan, Beverly K. <u>Explore the Wild: A Nature Search-and-Find Book.</u> HarperCollins Publishers, 1996. |
| Articles |
| "Hawks" <u>The Canadian Encyclopedia Vol. 2,</u> 1991. |

 Revise and Edit

Go back and review your research report.

- Ask a classmate or friend to look at your work. Listen to their suggestions. Are there ways to improve what you've done?
- Proofread your work for errors in spelling, punctuation, and grammar.
- Have you used complete sentences? capital letters for names and sentence beginnings? periods or questions marks at the end of sentences or questions?

 Think about Your Learning

Add your own questions about what makes a good report to this checklist.

- Did you select a subject that interests you?
- Did you use a variety of resources?
- Does your report have a beginning, a middle, and an end?
- Is each middle paragraph about one idea?
- Are there parts that need more information?

Unit 3: *Media Moments*

You wake up in the morning and the newspaper is at your door. You turn on the radio and the broadcaster is reading today's news. You turn on your television—more news!! All around you, people are recording events and telling you what is happening in the world. This is done through the media.

In this unit, you will look closely at a variety of news media, including TV, photographs, the Internet, newspapers, and magazines. You will see how they provide important information about what is happening in the world. By knowing more about the media, you will become a better judge of what you read, see, and hear in news reports. You will

- look at pictures for information and enjoyment
- learn about newspaper, Internet, and TV reporting
- compare the way different media cover the same event
- learn about different sections of a newspaper
- find out how people document events
- create your own newspaper page

TAMI'S SECRETS: An Informer Inside the Mob

CANADA'S WEEKLY NEWSMAGAZINE

SPECIAL SECTION
BATTLEGROUND ONTARIO

Maclean's

MAY 12, 199...

CANADA

1192

RED RIVER
COURAGE

...anitobans fought,
...y home,

C A P T U R E D
Moments

Written by Trudee Romanek
Illustrated by Steve MacEachern

READING TIP

Track sequence of events

This selection tells about the history of documenting or recording events. Articles such as this usually proceed from the beginning of an invention up to the present time. As you read, jot notes about each new method that people developed to record important events.

D
o you have a photo album? It's fun to look at old pictures of our families, but your photos have another purpose, too. Each image shows a moment of your life. It is proof that your cousin Lisa was at your fifth birthday party. Or it reminds you of that silly haircut your mom gave you in the second grade.

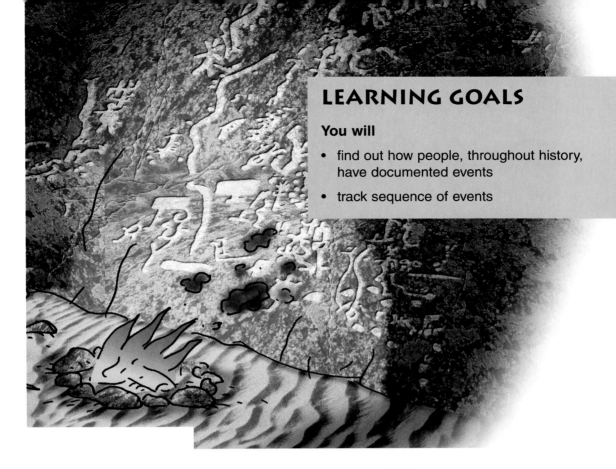

Long before there were cameras, people documented or recorded the events of their lives in other ways. Early peoples drew pictures on rocks and cave walls. Or they told stories of events to their children, who passed them on to their children, and so on.

133

When writing was invented, humans began recording events with written words, as well.

These days we have many different ways to document things happening in our world. Newspapers and magazines print articles about events as soon as they happen. Often they include photos as well. Television stations use videotape and audiotape to record events. Their cameras and microphones let TV viewers see and hear what is happening. It makes us feel as though we are at the events ourselves.

How do you document things in *your* life? Do you have a photo album? Perhaps you write the things you do or the way you feel in a diary or journal. Some families use an audio tape recorder to record the sounds of special occasions, such as birthday parties. Some even have video cameras to make home movies. So you may have photographs, videotapes, audiotapes, journals, and other things that tell the story of your life. It would be a lot easier if you could keep all of these documents in one place. With special computer equipment we can now do that.

Computer memory is a little like a photo album, journal, and videotape all rolled up in one tiny package. It is a big chunk of space for memories of just about any kind. You can store pictures, written words, audio recordings, and video recordings in computer memory. A lot can be stored on a computer's *hard drive,* the memory that is inside a computer. However, sometimes audio recordings and video recordings have to be stored as *large format removable media* on special disks because they take up lots of memory space.

Let's look at how one girl used the special equipment on her computer to document a summer trip.

My Computer Journal

by Yasmin Cheung

I wanted to make a journal of everything about my summer trip to Calgary. First, I typed in the words I had written in my journal on each day of our trip. Next, I got my photographs and drawings scanned. That means a special sort of photocopier turned the pictures into a computer file so I could show them on my computer. I placed each picture with the journal entry of the day I took it. Then I typed in a description of each photo so people looking at my journal would know what each one is.

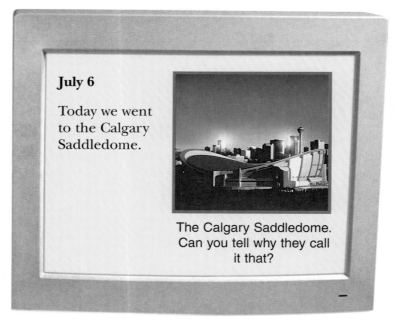

July 6

Today we went to the Calgary Saddledome.

The Calgary Saddledome. Can you tell why they call it that?

Mom helped me hook up our tape recorder to the computer so I could add tape recordings of things we heard on our trip. I programmed my journal so the correct recording plays when each picture comes up on the screen.

Then Dad hooked up the video camera to our computer so I could include the movies we took on our trip.

I'm very proud of my multimedia vacation journal. It was a lot of work, but it's great for telling people about our trip. I want to show it to my friends and family in other cities, too, so next week Dad's going to help me post it on our web site.

July 9

I learned today that Alberta's provincial bird is the Great Horned Owl. This is what it looks like.

The Great Horned Owl, Alberta's provincial bird.

July 10

Went to the Calgary Stampede! Was it ever fun! This is the video I took.

Click here to start the video.

AFTER YOU READ

Make a time line

Review the notes you made while reading. Make a time line to show the order of inventions that people found to record events. Start with the earliest method and finish with the present. Look for words that give you clues to the order of events, such as "in the beginning," "then," or "now."

Making History

Written by Monica Kulling
Photograph by Kathryn Hollinrake

Today is a holiday.
I hold a camera
and frame your face
whenever you look my way.

I line up light
to make you shine.
I line up you
to make you mine.

Move forward.
Move left.
Move back.
Move right.
Give yourself
to the camera's sight.

I focus. Re-focus.
It's sharp. Now sharper.
Your lines are true.
I hold my breath.
My breath holds you.

It's ready.
It's now.
It's ...

CLICK!

You're history.

MANITOBA
Flood Facts

Adapted from "1997 Manitoba Flood Facts" *by Travel Manitoba*
and "Red River Dance" *by Greg Pindera*

READING TIP

Use text features

Many information selections have special text features that stories do not have. Look carefully at the special features in this article—the headings, the time line, and the map. How do you think these features will help you to read this article?

Flood, fire, or earthquake, war or peace—when something happens that interests us, we depend on television, radio, newspapers, magazines, and the Internet for news and to help us understand what is going on.

In April 1997, the Red River flooded parts of Manitoba and the northern United States. Thousands of people living along its banks watched up-to-the-minute flood reports on local TV stations and prepared for the worst. At the same time, the rest of Canada and the world watched the mighty river and how local people responded.

Red River Flood History
Manitoba has had many floods. The rivers in southern Manitoba are narrow channels cutting through the flat prairie landscape. When the rivers rise, water pours over the sides of the riverbeds and floods the plain.

140

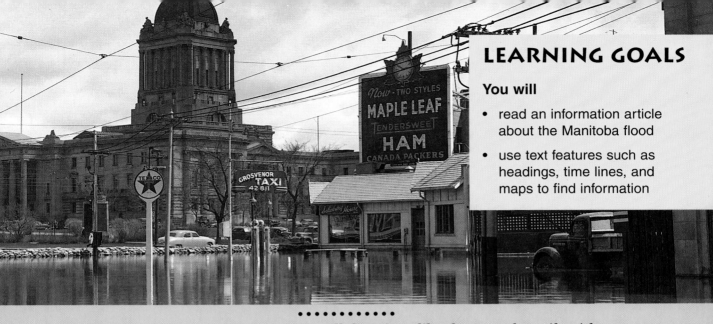

. . . .

"Houses and barns were floating in all directions like sloops under sail, with dogs, cats, and poultry in them. Outhouses, carts, carioles, boxes, cupboards, tables, chairs, feather beds, and every variety of household furniture drifting along added to the universal wreck."

—Alexander Ross, writing in his memoirs of the 1852 flood

. . . .

Manitoba Flood Levels

1826

The Red River floods—with a high point, or *crest,* 11.1 m above the riverbed. People, including 400 settlers around Fort Garry, flee what is still the worst recorded flood in Manitoba.

1950

A crest of 9.2 m forces 80 000 of Winnipeg's 400 000 people and almost 20 000 rural people to flee. After, 109 km of riverbanks are piled with clay and 31 pumping stations are built.

1997

The river floods again and crests at 7.5 m. Without the floodway, dams, and dikes that were built in the '60s and '70s, the crest might have reached 10.5 m, as shown above.

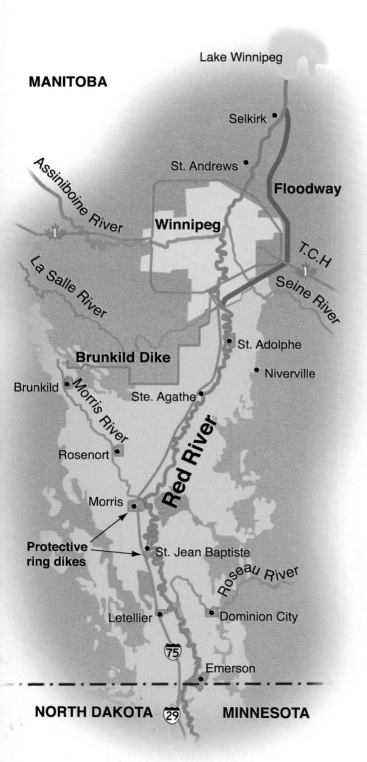

MANITOBA

Lake Winnipeg

Selkirk

St. Andrews

Floodway

Winnipeg

T.C.H

Assiniboine River

La Salle River

Seine River

Brunkild Dike

St. Adolphe

Niverville

Brunkild

Morris River

Ste. Agathe

Red River

Rosenort

Morris

Protective ring dikes

St. Jean Baptiste

Roseau River

Letellier

Dominion City

75

Emerson

NORTH DAKOTA 29 **MINNESOTA**

Crest

After much anticipation, the river crested in Winnipeg on May 3.

Evacuation

More than 28 000 Manitobans were evacuated from their homes when the floodwaters rose.

Date: May 1, 1997, 7:32 AM Local Time
Beam: Standard 6, Orbit: Descending

Sandbags

More than 8500 soldiers and thousands of civilian volunteers filled and stacked millions of sandbags along the riverbanks and around homes. This became one of the biggest military missions in Canadian history.

Ring Dikes

The permanent ring dikes built around eight rural communities succeeded. As the raging Red River swallowed thousands of hectares of farmland, the ring dikes withstood the waters to protect their communities.

Flooded Farms

The floodwaters covered 202 500 ha of farmland—about 5 per cent of the province's farmland.

Floodway
Nicknamed "Duff's Ditch" after the former Premier Duff Roblin, the floodway again helped protect Winnipeg from disastrous flooding.

Brunkild (or Z-) Dike
This 40-km dike was built quickly southwest of Winnipeg's Perimeter Highway to prevent flood waters from draining into the La Salle River and Winnipeg. More than 400 pieces of heavy equipment operated 24 hours a day to construct the z-shaped dike.

AFTER YOU READ

Use headings to find the main idea

Which text feature did you find most helpful? Writers often use headings to help the reader focus on the main idea of each section. Write down each heading and a sentence that summarizes what that section is about.

The RED RIVER FLOOD:
AN INTERNET JOURNAL

Written by Kathleen Easton and Gorden Chorney

READING TIP

Think about the source

Information on the Internet can either be factual or the opinion of the writer. As you read this journal, look for clues that tell you what parts are facts about the flood and what parts are the writers' opinions.

Kathleen Easton is a writer and Gorden Chorney is a photographer. They live in Winnipeg, Manitoba. In April 1997, they learned that the "flood of the century" was headed for southern Manitoba. They decided to document the events in a day-by-day journal of words and pictures. Kathleen and Gorden began a journey by car and small airplane. They followed the Red River from where it begins in North Dakota, United States, to where it empties into Lake Winnipeg. Kathleen and Gorden set up a web site, and every few days they published their reports and photographs on the Internet. During the flood, more than 30 000 people visited their web site to find out what was happening. Here are some portions from Kathleen and Gorden's Internet flood journal:

LEARNING GOALS

You will

- read a personal journal taken from the Internet
- compare fact and opinion

Back Forward Home Edit Reload Images Print Find Stop

Location: http://www

What's New? | What's Cool? | Destinations | Net Search | People | Software

April 3, 1997

We leave Winnipeg by car at 8:30 a.m. The weather is beautiful and the land is covered in snow. We are on our way to Wahpeton, North Dakota. That's where the Red River starts its long journey of 883 km northward. We drive from Canada into the United States and continue our journey south on Highway I-29. The Red River is on our left, hidden by trees. Three-quarters of the way to Grand Forks, North Dakota, we come across a strange sight.

Parked on an overpass are three helicopters painted flat black, people in uniform, and other types of military vehicles. State Troopers sit in their cars, blocking the roads leading to the overpass. A fourth helicopter swoops in and lands on one of the roads leading up to the overpass. Are we watching an invasion? No, just the U.S. National Guard using helicopters to put sandbags along the river.

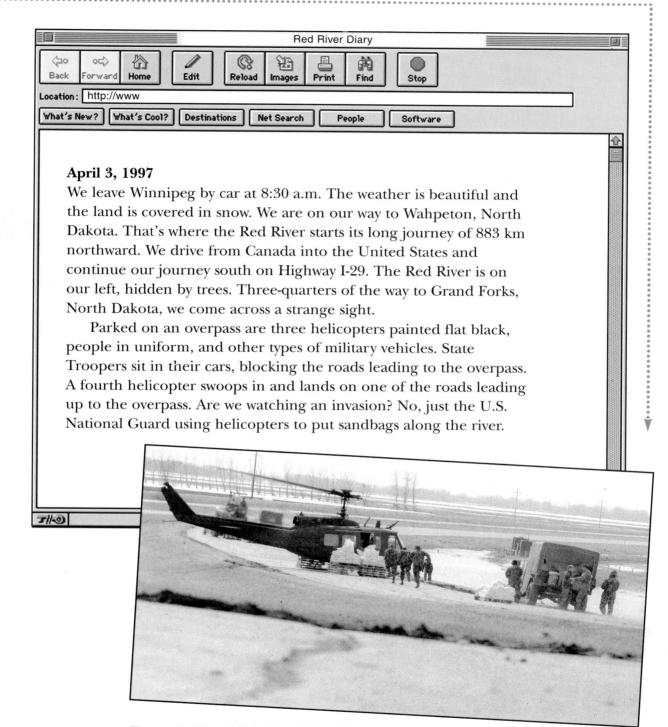

The goal of the U.S. National Guard is to sandbag 88 km of the Red River using about 20 000 sandbags.

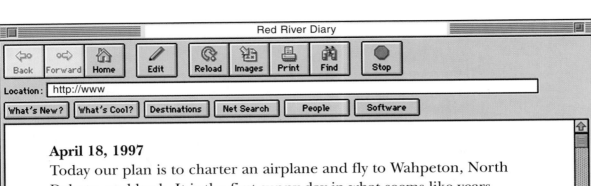

April 18, 1997

Today our plan is to charter an airplane and fly to Wahpeton, North Dakota, and back. It is the first sunny day in what seems like years.

It surprises me that Manitoba is still covered in snow. As far as the eye can see, the farmers' fields are completely white. We turn south to follow the Red River and fly over the floodway and St. Norbert, Manitoba. Here you can see the mammoth dikes they have been building to protect the town from the "flood of the century." We continue to follow the Red River. It looks like a giant snake in the way it twists and turns. In some parts you can see where the river has already started to creep inland over its banks.

Flying south from Canada to the United States you are in for a big shock. Almost immediately past the border you see the U.S. landscape covered in dirty brown water. Everywhere, the roads are flooded over. We can see the tops of trees along what used to be the banks of the Red River; that's the only way to tell where the river is. We often fly off course just because we lose sight of the river in the sea of water.

It is hard to show how wide the Red River is using photos. I hope this one gives a good idea of the damage.

Back | Forward | Home | Edit | Reload | Images | Print | Find | Stop

Location: http://www

What's New? | What's Cool? | Destinations | Net Search | People | Software

The worst of the flood seems over for Wahpeton. Quite a few houses closest to the river have only their roofs above the water. Three of the lanes of a four-lane highway are completely under water. There is an immense traffic jam.

We circle over Wahpeton a few times and start heading back north. South of Grand Forks we fly over two large chunks of ice. At first it looks as if there is garbage all over the place, but through our binoculars we can make out about 14 deer. With no place to go, the deer could starve to death.

Sam the dog and his doghouse are surviving the flood well in Wahpeton.

We spotted two groups of deer on high ground. We radioed authorities in North Dakota and someone was going to try to get some food to them. We hope they survive the flooding.

Location: http://www

What's New? | What's Cool? | Destinations | Net Search | People | Software

April 28, 1997: St. Norbert, Manitoba

I am writing this in a hurry because the people of St. Norbert, just south of Winnipeg, have to leave their homes by tomorrow at 8:00 p.m. Some friends in St. Norbert are packing to stay with family in Winnipeg. I have volunteered to take in their three cats. With the addition of these cats, I'll have a total of five cats, two turtles, one snake, and several tropical fish who call my townhouse home. I may have to find another place to stay if this keeps up.

As I write this, Gorden is photographing Canadian military personnel as they arrive in Winnipeg. Two hundred military vehicles are driving in tonight, with another 200 due tomorrow. There will be 6700 Army, Navy, and Air Force personnel in the city. That's more than the total of those involved in Canada's Peacekeeping Missions in the Middle East, Haiti, and Bosnia.

April 29, 1997: Winnipeg, Manitoba

We drive out to the "Z-Dike," a 40-km dike that is being built to protect the southwest corner of Winnipeg. ("Z-Dike" is a nickname for the Brunkild Dike. It is called this because, from the air, part of the dike looks exactly like the letter Z.) People are working frantically, in hope that the dike will stop overland flooding from reaching Winnipeg.

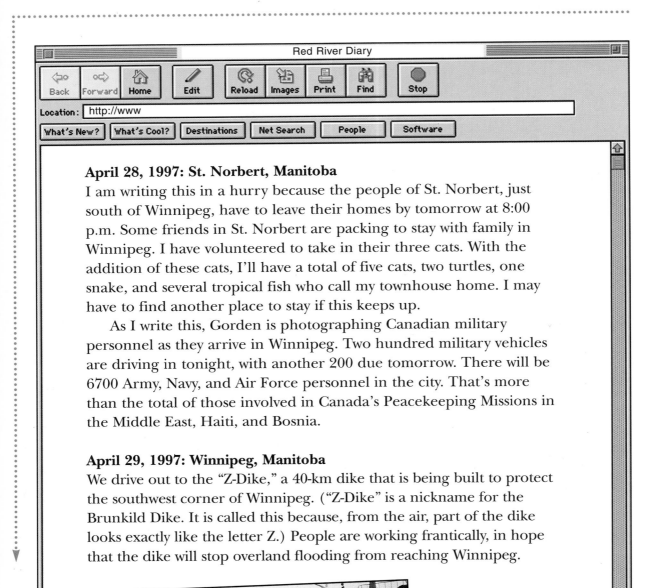

Equipment on the Brunkild Dike is working 24 hours a day to complete the work. There are bulldozers for as far as the eye can see.

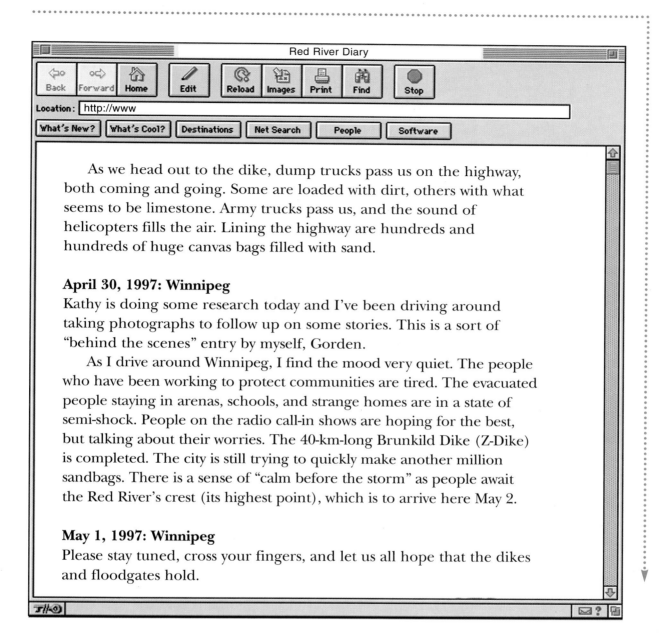

As we head out to the dike, dump trucks pass us on the highway, both coming and going. Some are loaded with dirt, others with what seems to be limestone. Army trucks pass us, and the sound of helicopters fills the air. Lining the highway are hundreds and hundreds of huge canvas bags filled with sand.

April 30, 1997: Winnipeg
Kathy is doing some research today and I've been driving around taking photographs to follow up on some stories. This is a sort of "behind the scenes" entry by myself, Gorden.

As I drive around Winnipeg, I find the mood very quiet. The people who have been working to protect communities are tired. The evacuated people staying in arenas, schools, and strange homes are in a state of semi-shock. People on the radio call-in shows are hoping for the best, but talking about their worries. The 40-km-long Brunkild Dike (Z-Dike) is completed. The city is still trying to quickly make another million sandbags. There is a sense of "calm before the storm" as people await the Red River's crest (its highest point), which is to arrive here May 2.

May 1, 1997: Winnipeg
Please stay tuned, cross your fingers, and let us all hope that the dikes and floodgates hold.

AFTER YOU READ

Compare fact and opinion

In this journal, find three examples of information that expresses the writers' opinions and three examples of factual information. Find evidence from the journal to support your choices.

Red River Courage:

A Triumph of Heart and Spirit in Manitoba

Written by Barry Came
From Maclean's *magazine*

READING TIP

Think like a writer

Magazine writers use "eye-catching" titles and pictures to get a reader's attention. What did this writer do to get your interest? As you read the article, look for things the writer does to keep your attention.

Ron Isaac's dark red pickup truck is parked at the end of a narrow country lane, right where the roadway disappears beneath a coffee-coloured sea. Inside the truck, the 62-year-old Manitoba farmer points toward a distant clump of trees. "That's my place over there," he says, matter-of-factly. "My seed bins are gone, water's up to the main floor around the house." He pushes the brim of a battered baseball cap from his brow, leans an elbow on the steering wheel. "You know I've lived in this valley since I was a boy, fought all the big floods." He ticks off the particularly bad years on the fingers of one hand—1950, 1966, 1979, 1996. "I thought I'd seen everything that old river could throw at me. But this one," he sighs, giving his head a single, tiny shake, "this one has been the great-granddaddy of them all."

The flood of the century, they have been calling it in Manitoba. The flood created a 2000-square-kilometre sea. It stretched all the way from the United States border to the southern suburbs of Winnipeg, 110 km to the north. The Red flowed over 800 farms and covered some of the richest soil in the country. Close to 25 000 residents fled their homes for higher ground. Masses of machinery and a huge army have been called upon to fight the menace. Thousands of civilians have helped out, as well as 8500 personnel from the Canadian Forces.

By Saturday evening, the battle seemed to be won. The Red's crest finally rolled into Winnipeg late on Thursday, May 1. The city's defences sprang a leak or two, but in the end they held. "Today is looking good," breathed a relieved Winnipeg Mayor Susan Thompson as she arrived in her office on Friday morning. "What happened in the past 24 hours is a pretty positive development."

Despite the relief, the danger has not yet completely

passed. The peril lies in several places. First, the height of the Red's water won't be going down for some time. "That crest is going to stay up there for the next four or five days," cautioned Larry Whitney, Manitoba's chief flood liaison officer, on May 2. Even when it does finally move on, Winnipeg will likely have high water levels for at least two or three more weeks.

The backup dikes are the most likely to fail. Volunteers worked around the clock to construct them, and in the past

153

few days soldiers from all across the country also helped. Most of these dikes are slapdash affairs, made from mud and strengthened with roughly eight million sandbags. The sand-filled white plastic sacks are so common a sight nowadays that local residents call them "Red River perogies." Noted Winnipeg's chief flood engineer Doug McNeil: "All sandbagged dikes leak at some point, and the longer the river remains high, the greater the chances of a leak."

Two shifts of 35 teams will check the backup dikes day and night. But there have already been dozens of leaks. On the

day the Red's crest rolled into Winnipeg, there were nine complete failures. Dozens of families had to move from threatened homes, including three apartment buildings in the downtown core.

Another possible threat lies southwest of Winnipeg along the newly built Brunkild dike. It runs from the point where the Red enters Winnipeg to the tiny hamlet of Brunkild. The dike, an eight-metre-high wall of mud and crushed rock, was built in just three weeks. Officials hope it will prevent the Red River from getting around Winnipeg's southern defences. They feared the water might swing west once it got to Winnipeg, and flow into the La Salle River. Then it could rush down the La Salle Valley to flood the capital from the west.

By the end of last week, the Red's bulging crest was lapping at the foot of the Brunkild dike. But the worst is yet to come. Provincial water resources engineers expect high water to hit the dike early this week. The rainfall and strong southerly winds that are forecast could

make the situation worse. Leaks in the barrier might mean trouble for Winnipeg's southern suburbs, especially the 4200 residents of St. Norbert.

St. Norbert lies just beyond the highway that rings Winnipeg. It would be right in the path of any water flowing from a hole in the Brunkild dike. To protect residents, Manitoba's authorities ordered everyone to leave the community last Tuesday. Early that morning, police and soldiers set up roadblocks to make sure everybody got out. At the same time, volunteers finished putting up a dike around St. Norbert church. This is the church where Father N. Ritchot and Louis Riel met on the night of October 21, 1869, to launch the Red River Rebellion. That rebellion eventually led to the founding of Manitoba.

A few blocks away, Riel's great-grandnephew, Joseph Riel, his wife, Joann, and his mother, Marie, were packing up their belongings. "Last week, we volunteered to help out in St. Adolphe," said Joseph. "We never dreamed that pretty soon they'd be volunteering to help us." His mother, pointing out that the family has been fighting Red River flooding for many generations, added: "But there has been nothing of the magnitude of this flood. When you see what happened in Ste. Agathe, it just gives you a chill."

Ste. Agathe met its fate in the early hours of Tuesday morning. The town of 500 sits on the west bank of the Red, 24 km due south of Winnipeg. It was protected by a dike running along the river's edge. But strong winds helped the flood wash over a highway and a raised set of railway tracks west of the community. "Essentially, the water came in the back door," said flood liaison officer Whitney. Ste. Agathe postmaster Jean Champagne, the last civilian to flee the town, recalled: "A big, massive body of water came jumping over the west side of the highway. You could feel it coming. It was gushing, just like when you hear running rapids."

Comments like that made people in Winnipeg and other communities work even harder to protect themselves against the flood. But although things were serious, an almost joyful feeling was running through all the preparations. This feeling was helped by the outpouring of support from the rest of the country. At the Brunkild dike, the troops of the Royal Canadian Horse Artillery seemed to be enjoying the entire affair. One soldier interrupted a lunch break to compare duty in Manitoba to that in war-torn Bosnia: "It's safer here and the food's a lot better."

In Winnipeg, thousands of people volunteered for sandbag duty. "Sandbagging at school wasn't as much fun as at Kingston Crescent," said 12-year-old Jenneke Juit. "It was snowing, we were in the mud, and we ended up about two feet from the river...," the girl continued. "I had mud in my hair, caked in. And the worms were coming out, getting frozen."

Dan Donahue, a Kingston Crescent resident, remembered the moment the volunteers, including young Jenneke, turned up. "It's a very emotional thing, especially those first moments when the first group of 100 or so people arrive at your door and start sandbagging," said the music producer. "At first, you feel, 'Oh, my nice quiet neighbourhood is overrun.' And then, when they're all gone, you find that you miss them."

In the meantime, Canadians across the country have been opening their wallets and their cupboards to help Manitoba's flood victims. The Red Cross said Friday that it wants to raise $10 million

through the Manitoba Flood Appeal. Dozens of corporations have already donated. In fact, the fund has raised $500 000 after three days. And on Friday morning, the citizens of Winnipeg donated $15 000 in just one hour in a telethon.

Help has been coming in all shapes and forms. The Toronto Blue Jays baseball team collected money, as did the Calgary Philharmonic Orchestra. In British Columbia, the Penticton Rotary club is sending bottled water donated by a Vancouver company. Residents of the Saguenay River Valley in Quebec, with last summer's disastrous floods fresh in their memory, raised $100 000. The CBC's Peter Gzowski staged a nationwide charity benefit on his radio show, *Morningside*.

Some people are saying that the public support of flood victims may actually be helping bring Canadians together. That may well be true. But if it is, some people have paid a terrible price for it. They are people like Red River farmer Ron Isaac, whose home and livelihood lie at the bottom of a shallow, muddy sea. "It's a very, very hard thing to bear," he mutters as he sits in his red pickup, staring across the churning water. Some trees mark all that remains of what was once his flourishing farm and business. Thousands of Manitobans share his troubles.

AFTER YOU READ

Note writer techniques

List three things the writer did to keep the reader interested in his article. Write them in your notebook. Under each item, note words or phrases that the author used to make the reader want to continue reading.

Headline *News*

Written by Alan Simpson

READING TIP

Make predictions

Newspaper headlines are written to catch the reader's attention. The first paragraph, called the *lead,* tells the reader the main idea of the article. Read the headlines that follow before you read any of the leads. Predict what the articles will be about.

W e can follow what is happening in an unfolding story like the Red River flood by reading the newspaper. But often we are in too much of a hurry to read a whole newspaper article. That's one reason newspaper writers place the most important information in a story in the headline and first paragraph. Here are some headlines and leads from the *Winnipeg Free Press* during the Manitoba flood of 1997.

LEARNING GOALS

You will

- read about how the media might exaggerate actual events

- learn to read newspaper headlines and leads

Flood defences on track in country, city

Getting ready

Dikes built to repel crest of approaching "lazy, old Red"

BY KIM GUTTORMSON

STAFF REPORTER

Manitoba is preparing for the flood—and time is on our side. Four of the eight communities in the Red River Valley are surrounded by dikes. The others will be finished in the next few days, well ahead of the Red River's crest.

Grand Forks under water

35 000 forced to flee; downtown
buildings burn

BY PAUL WIECEK

STAFF REPORTER

GRAND FORKS—As the worst flood in this area's history threatens Grand Forks, the city faces a new problem—fire. At least two major blazes were burning out of control downtown last night. Firefighters said they were helpless to do much about the fires. They couldn't get equipment into the area because of the high water.

THE RED ARRIVES

Flood to force 1000 to flee

BY BUD ROBERTSON, ALICE KRUEGER,
AND LEAH JANZEN

REPORTERS/CORRESPONDENT

The flood of the century invaded Manitoba yesterday. More than 1000 Red River Valley residents will be refugees by the end of today.

- *City set for worst—just in case*
- *Crews must close 16-km gap*

RACING THE RED

BY PAUL SAMYN, MANFRED JAGER,
AND MELANIE VERHAEGHE
REPORTERS/CORRESPONDENT

BRUNKILD—Dike builders have three days to win a 16-kilometre race with the Red River. The prize is the key to Winnipeg's back door. If the construction crews win the race, Sanford and La Salle will stay dry. But if they lose, the Red will get around the city's right side and pour down the La Salle River.

Wind our next foe

*Farms, towns threatened as waves
rise on "sea"*

BY DAVE SUPLEVE, RANDY TURNER,
AND ANDREW MAXWELL
STAFF REPORTERS/CORRESPONDENT

EMERSON—Winds gusted up to 60 kilometres an hour last night. They whipped the "Red Sea" into a fury and sent a new wave of fear across southern Manitoba.

Red's crest in city today

10 000 Winnipeggers put on evacuation alert

BY BRUCE OWEN, ALDO SANTIN, AND ALICE KRUEGER
STAFF REPORTERS

As the Red River prepares to crest here today, an anxious city waits. The crest is expected in downtown Winnipeg tonight, still at 7.5 metres. Forty hours later, it will likely put the Brunkild dike to the test.

The day was ours

Red scores minor victories

By Aldo Santin, Alice Krueger, and Bruce Owen
Staff Reporters

The Red River looked for weak spots in Winnipeg's flood defences yesterday, and it won some minor victories. But the day belonged to the city and its flood fighters, including the armed forces. The outlook was brighter last night than it had been 24 hours earlier.

"Pins and needles for next two weeks"

City says we can't let our guard down

By Kevin Rollason, Bill Redekop,
and Alice Krueger
Staff Reporters

There was a sense yesterday that the flood crisis was over. But city officials warned it was too soon to relax. The city's rivers remain brim-full. "We're still being very watchful," said Mayor Susan Thompson. "We're still on pins and needles for the next two weeks at least."

EYE ON **MEDIA**

Written by Todd Mercer

MUCH OF THE NEWS COVERAGE OF THE 1997 MANITOBA FLOOD focused on how the floodwaters threatened Winnipeg. Did the media make the danger to Winnipeg seem worse than it really was? Some flood experts and media critics think so.

The picture below appeared in many Canadian newspapers and in television news stories about Red River flooding. It shows the flood damage suffered in Grand Forks, North Dakota. Here the flood caused about one billion dollars damage. Flood experts think one reason for this great amount of destruction was that the floodwater levels were about a metre higher than expected—enough to badly flood the city.

Several media stories about southern Manitoba flood conditions used the Grand Forks flood photograph, even though the situations were very different.

In Canada, flood experts' predictions about the water levels were more accurate than they had been in Grand Forks. And in the Winnipeg area, the Red River Floodway was available to take away large amounts of water and keep Winnipeg safe from major flooding.

Was it right for the media to use the Grand Forks photograph in stories about southern Manitoba flood danger? Reporter John Collision says "No." He feels the media took one picture of Grand Forks and used it to exaggerate Manitoba flood conditions.

Jay Deoring, an engineer at the University of Manitoba agrees. He thinks the media coverage of the story failed to report the strength of Winnipeg's flood defences, such as the Red River Floodway.

Other people were also critical of the media reports. "Watching TV news, you get really frustrated and scared," said one person who had evacuated his home largely because of frightening television news reports.

Misleading news flood reports had effects in other areas of Canada and the world. Some music concerts, business conventions, and even the national Special Olympics were cancelled or postponed because people planning to attend saw only the worst flood pictures. Flooding didn't even affect areas where these events were to be held.

What do you think? Did the national media go too far in repeatedly using the Grand Forks picture in southern Manitoba flood news coverage?

Media
AT ITS BEST

Written by Jake MacDonald
From Maclean's *magazine*

As more than 300 media teams converged on the big story, many Winnipeggers found the best TV coverage on an all-volunteer community-access channel, Cable 11. About 170 extra people signed up to help provide programming around the clock for 16 days—everything from the mayor's news conferences and live reports from flooded areas to lessons in how to fill sandbags.

AFTER YOU READ

Check your predictions

How well were you able to predict from the headlines? Think about what you read in "Eye on Media." Do you think that newspaper headlines can be used to make events seem even more important or more dangerous than they really are? Write a paragraph to explain your opinion.

What's in a Newspaper?

Written by Susan Green

READING TIP

Think about what you know

Make a chart that lists all the newspaper sections you know. Include a brief description of the kind of information found in each section. As you read, think about what other sections and new information you can add to your chart.

Wherever you live in Canada, your local newspaper can keep you in touch with what is happening in your community, your country, and the world. Every day it brings you new information about events, sports, business, people, lifestyle, and entertainment.

LEARNING GOALS

You will

- read different sections of a newspaper

- learn the important features of each section of a newspaper

Mars landing bouncy perfect

One of the first images sent from the Mars Pathfinder shortly after it landed on July 4. NASA officials hope to use the exploration vehicle, known as a rover, to explore the planet's rocky surface.

Airbag that protected Pathfinder now keeping rover from setting down

BY STEPHEN STRAUSS
SCIENCE REPORTER

PASEDENA, Calif.— Humankind landed again on Mars and what it saw was a much more varied terrain than previously seen.

The first images of the Ares Vallis flood plain, where the Pathfinder landed looked like a vast, jumbled glacial boulder field.

In the distance, NASA scientists could see what they hadn't observed during the Viking lander visits to Mars in the 1970s—several hills perhaps up to a kilometre high.

After a seven-month, 497-million-kilometre voyage, one downside in Pathfinder's epic trip was that the craft seemed to have landed on a small mound, 45 centimetres off the ground.

↑ Newspapers include many different news stories. The size of the headline tells you how important each article is. The most important article is usually at the top of the page.

The front page of the newspaper also provides an index that tells you where to find the sections that interest you most. →

INDEX

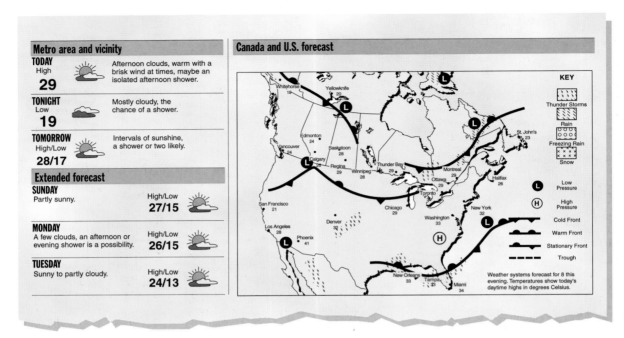

Metro area and vicinity

TODAY
High
29
Afternoon clouds, warm with a brisk wind at times, maybe an isolated afternoon shower.

TONIGHT
Low
19
Mostly cloudy, the chance of a shower.

TOMORROW
High/Low
28/17
Intervals of sunshine, a shower or two likely.

Extended forecast

SUNDAY
Partly sunny.
High/Low
27/15

MONDAY
A few clouds, an afternoon or evening shower is a possibility.
High/Low
26/15

TUESDAY
Sunny to partly cloudy.
High/Low
24/13

Canada and U.S. forecast

KEY
Thunder Storms
Rain
Freezing Rain
Snow
L Low Pressure
H High Pressure
Cold Front
Warm Front
Stationary Front
Trough

Weather systems forecast for 8 this evening. Temperatures show today's daytime highs in degrees Celsius.

⬆ All newspapers contain information about the weather. You can find out if it's likely to rain in your area tomorrow, or see what the weather is like in other parts of Canada and the world.

O, Canada! We have lots to appreciate

BY GARY LAUTENS

Time out.

For the next three minutes forget the complaints, the faults, the problems.

No sad songs today.

Let us count our blessings as Canadians.

We've got a vast land filled with natural resources, bustling cities, gorgeous mountains, prairies with sweet earth as far as you can see. We've got oceans to fish and more than our share of blue sky.

We have Nature as our friend.

We are outraged by injustice. It is not a luxury all people enjoy.

Our schools have books and trained teachers. Kids can dream big in Canada.

⬆ Newspapers across the country have writers or columnists who provide their views on world issues or everyday family life. They often use humour to describe what is happening around them.

The impact of technology

Isn't it astonishing how things are changing to make our lives easier.

Like in the communication and transportation fields for instance.

Communication has changed dramatically. It only seems like yesterday when I was forced to use a big, old, rotary dial telephone, sharing a party line with someone else and—in order to talk to an outside line—you had to go through an operator.

Nowadays, rather than having to talk to someone over a land line, we can simply use a compact cellular phone, throw a fax in the machine, or go on the Internet and e-mail.

↑ An editorial is written by the publisher of a newspaper. In this column, the publisher states his or her personal opinion on issues in the community, nation, or the world.

Thanks for the summer camp

Editor:

I would like to take this time to thank all the hardworking people who worked at the Summer Camp this year at the Drop-in Centre.

You all did a great job. Also, thanks to the Municipality of Rankin Inlet for funding the program.

My children enjoyed the activities and I hope more programs like these are funded once again. Thanks.

Laura Kowmuk

↑ Letters to the editor are written by readers of the newspapers. This section of the paper gives them a place to express their opinions about what they have read in the paper and what is happening in the world around them.

Diana 1961-1997

©INGRID

INGRID RICE/VANCOUVER

↑ Editorial cartoons can send a serious or powerful message to readers about events in the world. They can also find humour in political or social situations.

↑ Classified ads are a place for readers to advertise items they want to sell. You'll see cars, computers, homes, and many other things listed here. Employers use the classifieds to advertise jobs that are available.

BACK IN TRAINING: Marnie McBean to return to competitive rowing. Story, E6.

INSIDE

Sports Digest, E3

Grizzlies and Raptors play annual Naismith Game, E4

World Series resumes tonight, E5

Canadian Nancy Harvey second in LPGA, E8

← In the sports section of the newspaper, you will find out what is happening with your favourite sports team. You will also find information on many different types of sports events and tournaments.

American League standings

Thursday's results
Texas 6, Toronto 2
Baltimore 5, N.Y. Yankees 2
Seattle 9, Minnesota 6
Detroit 5, Anaheim 4
11 innings
Kansas City 7, Oakland 6
12 innings
Wednesday's results
N.Y. Mets 4, Toronto 2
Detroit 12, Atlanta 4
Chicago Cubs 10, Minnesota 6
Cleveland 7, Pittsburgh 3
Florida 7, Baltimore 6
Wild-card race

	W	L	Pct	
N.Y.	79	59	.572	—
Anaheim	74	66	.529	6
Milwaukee	70	68	.507	9
Toronto	65	74	.468	14 1/2

EAST

	W	L	Pct	Gb	Last 10	Streak	Home	Div
Baltimore	86	51	.628	—	3-7	W1	41-26	18-15
New York	79	59	.572	7 1/2	2-8	L4	39-28	14-12
Boston	67	73	.479	20 1/2	3-7	L6	33-38	17-18
Detroit	66	73	.475	21	6-4	W2	37-33	16-20
TORONTO	65	74	.468	22	2-8	L7	33-37	18-18

CENTRAL

	W	L	Pct	Gb	Last 10	Streak	Home	Div
Cleveland	72	63	.533	—	6-4	W1	37-32	21-9
Milwaukee	70	68	.507	3 1/2	7-3	L1	43-26	17-18
Chicago	69	70	.496	5	6-4	L2	38-30	17-11
Kansas C.	57	80	.416	16	5-5	L3	29-40	11-23
Minnesota	57	81	.413	16 1/2	5-5	L3	30-40	15-20

WEST

	W	L	Pct	Gb	Last 10	Streak	Home	Div
Seattle	77	63	.550	—	4-6	W1	39-31	15-10
Anaheim	74	66	.529	3	3-7	L3	41-29	19-6
Texas	67	73	.479	10	5-5	W3	34-36	9-16
Oakland	54	86	.386	23	3-7	L1	31-38	7-18

LOOKING AHEAD
   Saturday—Chicago White Sox at Cleveland, 1:05 p.m.; Anaheim at Detroit, 1:05 p.m.; Milwaukee at Boston, 1:05 p.m.; Baltimore at N.Y. Yankees, 1:05 p.m.; **Texas at Toronto, 4:05 p.m.**; Seattle at Minnesota, 8:05 p.m.; Oakland at Kansas City, 8:05 p.m.

↑ Statistics like those listed in the American League baseball chart show where your team is in the standings.

"Four thumbs up!!"—*The Weekly*

⬆ In the entertainment section, you will find news stories, reviews, and advertisements about concerts, movies, and plays.

⬆ If you live in the city, you will read a chart to see when each movie is playing in each cinema.

⬆ Comic strips are a common feature in newspapers. Many comics are "syndicated," meaning the same comic appears in many newspapers across the country.

Newspapers provide a community with lots of valuable information. How long do you think it would take you to read the whole newspaper? Perhaps an hour? Perhaps more? While television newscasts can provide us with news of the day, they don't have time to go into as much detail as a newspaper article can. And TV news can't give readers as many ways to respond. Can you think of other ways that newspapers and TV news are different?

AFTER YOU READ

Compare newspaper sections

Complete your chart by adding new information. What newspaper sections do you like to read best? What features make those sections interesting to you? What section of the paper do you read least? What features make it unattractive to you?

Making a

Written by Piero Ventura
Illustrated by Scot Ritchie

Weeklies, biweeklies, monthlies—every day many different kinds of publications arrive at newsstands. They put on a splendid show with all their glossy colorful covers. Newspapers, however, have a very different life. They are bought and read just a few hours after the news happens. The news office always has an open door to the world. The publisher's job is to oversee the general running of the office; together with the editors, he or she selects the news to be included and makes sure that it gets written up and printed on time.

Newspaper

Every daily paper has section heads, who are responsible for preparing the items included in their section: politics, local news, foreign news, sports, and entertainment. The hours in the news office pass in frenetic activity. Decisions about which news items are to be included in the next day's edition are made in the early afternoon, and later all the stories written or sent in by reporters and correspondents come in. By 8:00 p.m. the newspaper is roughly blocked out to show where each story, headline, photograph, and advertisement will go in the final edition. News items continue to arrive, and the layout is changed to make room for important updates until the very last minute. Finally, the newspaper is put to bed—printed.

AFTER YOU READ

Use clues to find word meaning

Review your list of new words. Now go back and see what clues the writer gave to help you understand the meaning of the words. Write each word and beside it explain what clues you used to figure out the meaning.

And Now, Sports with BARB ONDRUSEK....

Written by Todd Mercer

READING TIP

Ask questions

Interviews are one way reporters prepare news stories. Make a list of your criteria for good interview questions. If you could interview a sportscaster, what would you ask? As you read, compare your questions to those of Todd Mercer.

Barb Ondrusek is a sports journalist for Toronto's CBC television channel. She was once an international-calibre swimmer and middle-distance runner. After an injury ended Barb's athletic career, she realized that she wanted to tell stories about amateur and professional athletes.

For seven years she worked as a news reporter in Newfoundland, Halifax, Sudbury, and Windsor before settling in Toronto. Barb feels that the skills she learned as a news reporter have been very important to her success as a sports journalist.

I talked with Barb Ondrusek about sports journalism, then followed her through an ordinary working day.

Barb, what is your most memorable sports interview?
I guess it would be my first big NHL hockey interview with Jacques Demers. He was the coach of the Detroit Red Wings at the time. I was so nervous that the microphone was shaking in my hand.

The interview was on videotape, not live. After the first recording of the interview, Jacques told me to take a deep breath. He said, "That was pretty rough. You want me to get you some water? Then, we can try it again."

Where do you get ideas for your sports stories?

Sometimes people call me with ideas. Or I might come across someone whose friend or aunt knows a great athlete. But most of my story ideas come through contacts, conversations, reading, and research.

Barb interviews hockey player Paul Henderson, best known for scoring the winning goal in the Canada–Russia hockey series in 1972.

What do you have to think about when putting together a story?

Time is key. You do the best story you possibly can with the limited time you have. Today we did a story about a local athlete who's about to sign a big contract with a National Football League team.

For that story, I had two minutes and thirty seconds. An average news story on our program is about a minute and twenty seconds. My story was more of a feature piece.

To create the story, we shot footage of the athlete for three hours. We'd start the camera, stop for a while, then start it again. We caught him in different situations such as lifting weights and horsing around with a friend. I came back with an hour and a half of tape that I had to edit down to two and a half minutes.

175

How do you keep your sports reports within the required time?

I practise reading my report before I go on air. I time myself with a stopwatch to see how long everything will take. When I do the six o'clock news, I have about seven minutes altogether. When I do my eleven p.m. report, I have six minutes, so I have to go back and edit my videos and the number of words I say.

Why do you think some sports are popular on television while others aren't?

Because some sports carry better visually on television. My sport, swimming, bores a lot of people. According to the TV ratings, people only watch it during major competitions like the Olympics.

Many people would rather watch a hockey game because it's high-spirited, fast moving, and requires lots of skill.

With swimming, the athlete is in the water. The camera shots are all wide angle, which means they're distant shots. You're not up there close with the swimmer. In hockey, there are a lot of close-ups. The audience wants to relate to the game and players.

What are the major responsibilities of a television sports journalist?

To present the story accurately. Telling the truth is very important. So many times that doesn't happen. In some cases, I've been to the same game or press conference as other people in the sports media. But when their stories come out, they're entirely different from mine. They might use a quotation out of context to create a wrong or unfavourable impression of an athlete. Or they only present stories with catchy video clips or headlines.

What do you like most about your job?

Being able to tell the truth. And I enjoy getting a story that no one else has covered. Like the story about the local athlete, Otis Santiago, who's about to join the NFL. I got that story through my own digging. No other television sports program in Toronto had a story on him. That brings me a lot of satisfaction.

A Day in the Work Life of Barb Ondrusek

9:00 a.m.   I check the sports wires on the computer and read the sports sections of the major newspapers.

9:30 a.m.   I go with a camera operator to Pickering, Ontario, to shoot film for a story on Otis Santiago, the only Canadian player to be drafted in the first three rounds of the 1997 National Football League draft.

12:30 p.m.   We return to the CBC studio in downtown Toronto. There I edit an hour and a half of tape for my two and a half minute feature for the six o'clock evening news.

1:30 p.m.   As I'm writing the script for the Otis Santiago story, I also watch the world hockey championships from Finland.

177

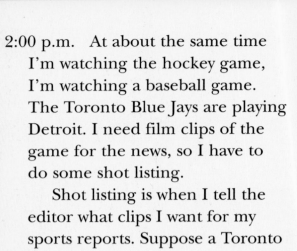

2:00 p.m. At about the same time I'm watching the hockey game, I'm watching a baseball game. The Toronto Blue Jays are playing Detroit. I need film clips of the game for the news, so I have to do some shot listing.

Shot listing is when I tell the editor what clips I want for my sports reports. Suppose a Toronto Blue Jay player hits a home run. I write on a slip of paper when that happened in the game and the word "Copy." Then I give the slip of paper to our editor. I might say, "I need seven seconds of this highlight and eight seconds of that highlight."

Our control room has many different TV sets. On an average night, I'm watching three games at any one time—maybe more.

4:30 p.m. All through the afternoon, I'm making calls and working on stories for the future. I'm always planning my stories for the next day, and the day after that.

6:20 p.m. I give my evening news sports report. It lasts about seven minutes.

6:30 p.m.–11:00 p.m. I'm lining up what games I need recorded for the 11 p.m. news. All through the evening I'm watching many games, shot listing important game events, and writing new introductions for my evening news report.

11:20 p.m. My late night sports report. It lasts about six minutes.

11:30 p.m. I make more phone calls confirming my stories for the next morning.

12:45 a.m. I get to go home.

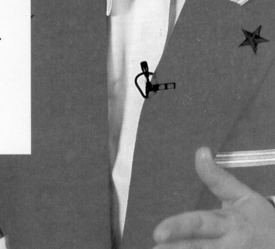

AFTER YOU READ

Review questions

Look carefully at the questions the interviewer asked. Go back to the list you created. Did Todd Mercer's questions match your criteria? Would you add any items to your list?

Challenge of Champions:

A MEDIA SPORTS EVENT

Written by Alan Simpson

READING TIP

Think about what you know

Think about a sporting event that was promoted by the media. Give examples of how the media attracted attention. As you read the web pages that follow, note all the ways in which the media generated interest in this event.

On June 1, 1997, Canadian Olympic champion Donovan Bailey and American Olympic runner Michael Johnson raced each other to see who was "The World's Fastest Man." The race itself was over in less than 15 seconds—Bailey won. Not only did Bailey and Johnson race, but the world's best track and field athletes also competed one-to-one in the three-hour "Challenge of Champions." The athletic contests were part of a huge media event. There was a parade, a party, a charity fundraiser, and a musical performance.

Let's look at some of the information placed on the Internet during the months before the big race. It will help us investigate the role of the media in a sport—track and field—that usually makes it onto television and into newspapers only during the Olympics.

Let's start by looking at some sections of the Donovan Bailey World Wide Web site:

Back | Forward | Home | Edit | Reload | Images | Print | Find

Location: http://www

What's New? | What's Cool? | Destinations | Net Search | People

Donovan Bailey WWWebsite

Memories etched in gold

Born: December 16, 1967, Manchester, Jamaica
Hometown: Oakville, Ontario, Canada
Height: 182 cm/6 ft Weight: 83 kg/182 lb

Donovan Bailey began running for Canada in 1994. Since then, he has become one of the world's greatest athletes. His proudest achievement occurred in 1996 at the Atlanta Summer Olympics. He shattered the world record in the 100 metre race. Donovan's speed then made it possible for the Canadian 4 x 100 m relay team to win the gold medal. This ended the United States' Olympic track-and-field winning streak. This page celebrates this Canadian athletic hero.

"The Sprint for a Mint"

June 1 is the definite date for the race between Donovan Bailey and Michael Johnson. The match will be held at Toronto's SkyDome. It is being called "The Sprint for a Mint" because each athlete will earn $500 000 just for running the 150 metre race and the first to cross the finish line will be rewarded a cool one million dollars.

QUICK FACTS
- Personal Bests
  100 m—9.84 s World Record
  4 x 100 m relay—37.69 s Canadian Record
  50 m indoor—5.56 s World Record
- Recorded a top speed of 43.4 km/h at the '96 Olympic Games.
- 1995—100 m and 4 x 100 World Champion
- 1996—100 m and 4 x 100 Olympic and World Champion
- First Canadian since 1928 to win the Olympic 100 m sprint.
- Off the track, Donovan owns a stockbroking, management, and construction company.

LEARNING GOALS

You will

- read information about a sports event from web sites

- learn how the media attracts attention to sporting events

Now let's examine information from the "ONE-to-ONE Challenge of Champions" web site:

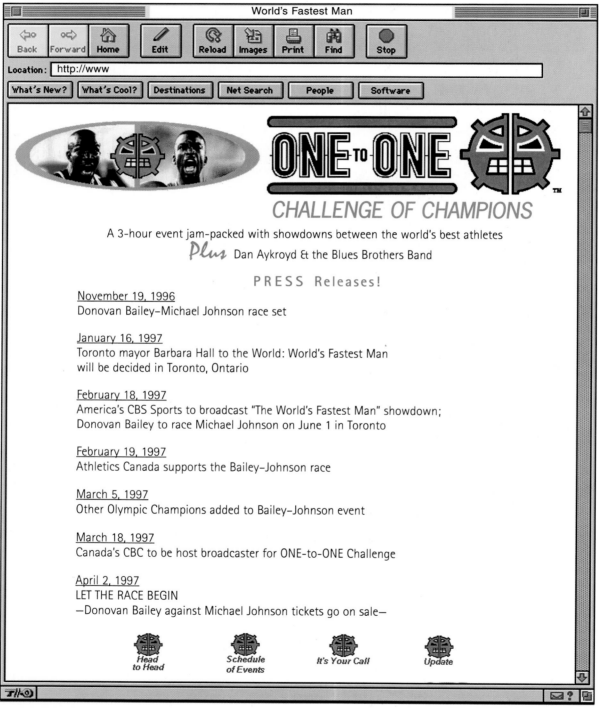

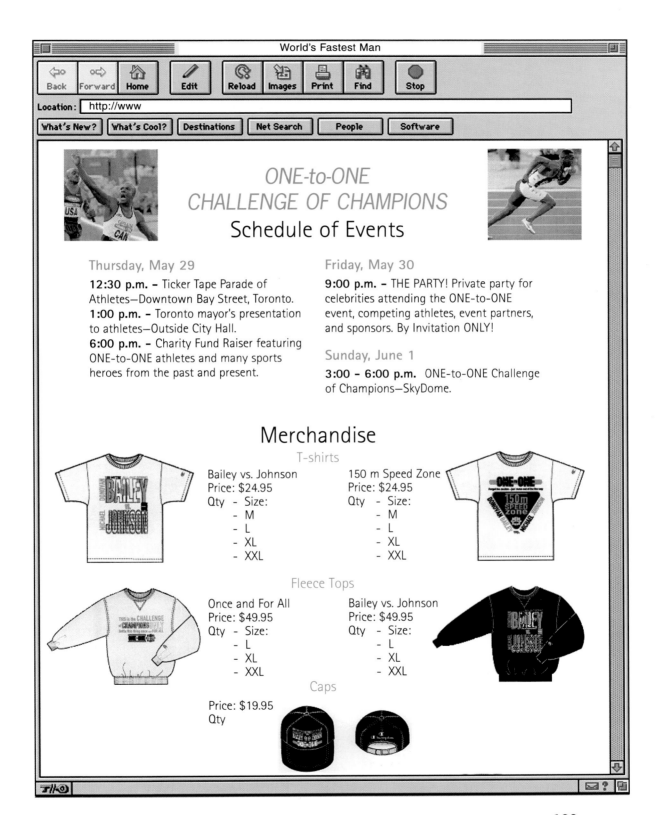

ONE-to-ONE CHALLENGE OF CHAMPIONS
Schedule of Events

Thursday, May 29

12:30 p.m. – Ticker Tape Parade of Athletes—Downtown Bay Street, Toronto.
1:00 p.m. – Toronto mayor's presentation to athletes—Outside City Hall.
6:00 p.m. – Charity Fund Raiser featuring ONE-to-ONE athletes and many sports heroes from the past and present.

Friday, May 30

9:00 p.m. – THE PARTY! Private party for celebrities attending the ONE-to-ONE event, competing athletes, event partners, and sponsors. By Invitation ONLY!

Sunday, June 1

3:00 – 6:00 p.m. ONE-to-ONE Challenge of Champions—SkyDome.

Merchandise
T-shirts

Bailey vs. Johnson
Price: $24.95
Qty - Size:
- M
- L
- XL
- XXL

150 m Speed Zone
Price: $24.95
Qty - Size:
- M
- L
- XL
- XXL

Fleece Tops

Once and For All
Price: $49.95
Qty - Size:
- L
- XL
- XXL

Bailey vs. Johnson
Price: $49.95
Qty - Size:
- L
- XL
- XXL

Caps

Price: $19.95
Qty

Location: http://www

World's Fastest Man

Here are some purpose statements for the Challenge of Champions event—from its web site:

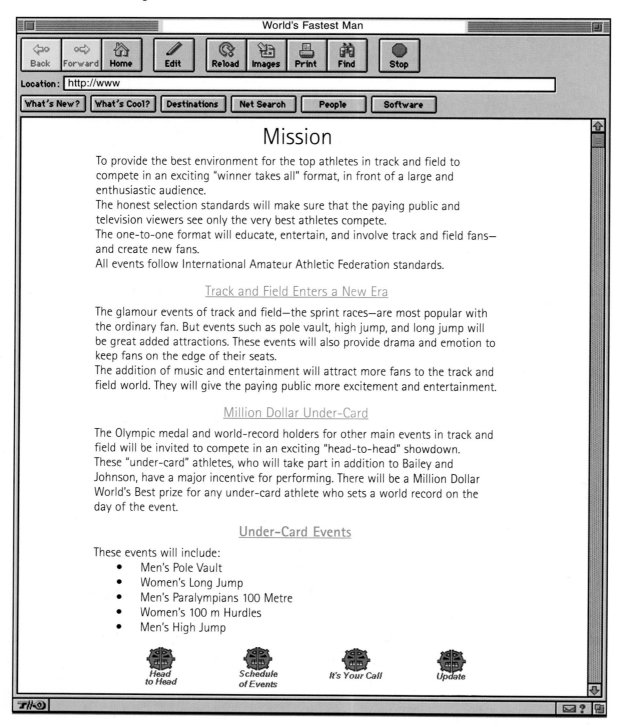

Mission

To provide the best environment for the top athletes in track and field to compete in an exciting "winner takes all" format, in front of a large and enthusiastic audience.

The honest selection standards will make sure that the paying public and television viewers see only the very best athletes compete.

The one-to-one format will educate, entertain, and involve track and field fans—and create new fans.

All events follow International Amateur Athletic Federation standards.

Track and Field Enters a New Era

The glamour events of track and field—the sprint races—are most popular with the ordinary fan. But events such as pole vault, high jump, and long jump will be great added attractions. These events will also provide drama and emotion to keep fans on the edge of their seats.

The addition of music and entertainment will attract more fans to the track and field world. They will give the paying public more excitement and entertainment.

Million Dollar Under-Card

The Olympic medal and world-record holders for other main events in track and field will be invited to compete in an exciting "head-to-head" showdown. These "under-card" athletes, who will take part in addition to Bailey and Johnson, have a major incentive for performing. There will be a Million Dollar World's Best prize for any under-card athlete who sets a world record on the day of the event.

Under-Card Events

These events will include:
- Men's Pole Vault
- Women's Long Jump
- Men's Paralympians 100 Metre
- Women's 100 m Hurdles
- Men's High Jump

Head to Head   **Schedule of Events**   **It's Your Call**   **Update**

Well, you've seen some sample information about the ONE-to-ONE Challenge of Champions. How would you describe this event? Was it a sports competition? Was it entertainment? a way to make money? news? What do you think?

AFTER YOU READ

Make a personal response

Do you think that this was a sports event, an entertainment event, or a way to make money? Write a paragraph to explain your opinion. Give examples from the web sites to support your opinion.

Media Moments

In this unit, you have learned about the ways media document events. You also found out that the media present information from different points of view. This awareness can make you a better reader and viewer of media and media events. Now it is your turn to use all you have learned to make your own media product: a personal one-page newspaper.

▶ Before You Begin

Think about what you read in the selections about newspapers in this unit. Ask yourself these questions:

- What sections will I include in my newspaper?
- What can I write about my life that will be interesting to others?
- What will I call my newspaper?
- Who will read my newspaper?

You may want to use a web to organize your thoughts.

Here is the web that Julia created.

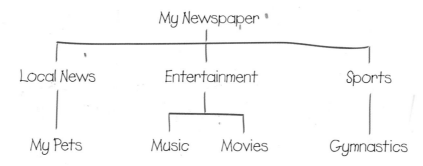

My Newspaper

Local News — Entertainment — Sports

My Pets — Music — Movies — Gymnastics

▶ Your First Draft

1 **Decide which sections you will include.**

- Think about the sections of a newspaper you read about in this unit.
- Look at newspapers you have at home.

2 **Write the text for each section of your newspaper.**

- Write headlines for each article.
- Outline the content of each article before you begin to write.
- Be an editor. Check that your articles are clearly written.

3 **Design your newspaper.**

- Decide on a name for your newspaper.
- Create a masthead design.
- Sketch a layout to show where you will place each article on the page.
- Choose pictures and illustrations that will appeal to your readers.

> ### Possible Sections for Your Newspaper
>
> - Ideas
> - Sports
> - Entertainment
> - Family
> - Cartoons

An AMAZING LIFE!

Volume 1, Issue 1   September 19

▶ Put It All Together

Decide how you will publish your newspaper.

Julia decided to create her newspaper on a computer.

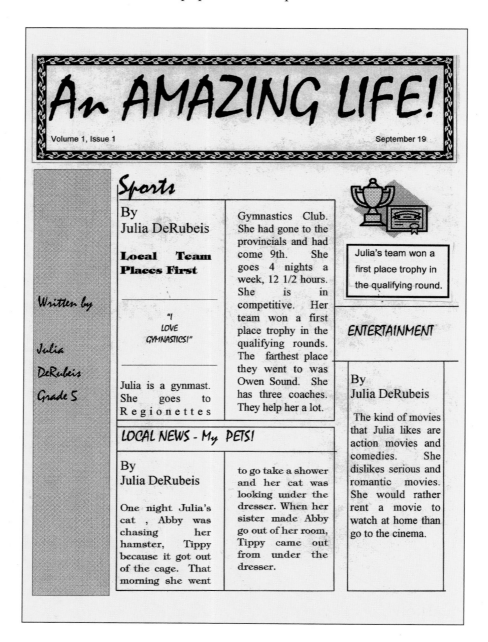

An AMAZING LIFE!

Volume 1, Issue 1   September 19

Written by

Julia
DeRubeis
Grade 5

Sports

By
Julia DeRubeis

Local Team Places First

"I LOVE GYMNASTICS!"

Julia is a gynmast. She goes to Regionettes Gymnastics Club. She had gone to the provincials and had come 9th. She goes 4 nights a week, 12 1/2 hours. She is in competitive. Her team won a first place trophy in the qualifying rounds. The farthest place they went to was Owen Sound. She has three coaches. They help her a lot.

Julia's team won a first place trophy in the qualifying round.

ENTERTAINMENT

By
Julia DeRubeis

The kind of movies that Julia likes are action movies and comedies. She dislikes serious and romantic movies. She would rather rent a movie to watch at home than go to the cinema.

LOCAL NEWS - My PETS!

By
Julia DeRubeis

One night Julia's cat , Abby was chasing her hamster, Tippy because it got out of the cage. That morning she went to go take a shower and her cat was looking under the dresser. When her sister made Abby go out of her room, Tippy came out from under the dresser.

Ways to Publish

- a computer printout
- a one-page flyer
- a class bulletin-board display
- the Internet
- a class newspaper

If your class decides to work together to make a newspaper, you will need to choose people to do different jobs.

- editor
- photographer
- reporter
- designer

Think about including advertising for your friends, family, and local businesses. You will also have to think about how to copy and distribute your newspaper.

Revise and Edit

Go back and review what you have included in your newspaper.

- Does it document your life in an interesting way?
- Ask a classmate or friend to look at your work. Listen to their suggestions. Are there ways to improve what you've done?
- Proofread your work for errors in spelling, punctuation, and grammar.
- Have you used complete sentences? capital letters for names and sentence beginnings? periods or question marks at the end of sentences or questions?

Think about Your Learning

Add your own ideas about what makes a good newspaper.

- Does each article fit with a section of a newspaper?
- Will your headlines hook the reader?
- Have you used pictures to make your newspaper more appealing?
- Are there details you could add to your articles to make them more interesting?

ACKNOWLEDGMENTS

Permission to reprint copyrighted material is gratefully acknowledged. Every effort has been made to trace ownership of all copyrighted material and to secure permission from copyright holders. In the event of any question arising as to the use of any material, we will be pleased to make the necessary corrections in future printings.

Photographs
pp. 76-77 © Jim Brandenburg/First Light; p. 87 courtesy of the Task Force to Bring Back the Don; pp. 89-91 © Patrice Halley; p. 95 © Jim Brandenburg/First Light; p. 103 courtesy of the North Island Wildlife Recovery Association; p. 104 courtesy of Ontario Ministry of Natural Resources, Copyright: 1997 Queens Printer, Ontario; p. 105 © Dick Hemingway; p. 106 (bottom) courtesy of Ontario Ministry of Natural Resources; p. 107 courtesy of the Long Point Bird Observatory; p. 109 courtesy of Heather Tonner; p. 110 Dave Starrett; p. 112 courtesy of Linda Doody; pp. 118-119 © Kelvin Aitken/First Light; pp. 130-131 (centre) Dave Starrett; p. 131 (bottom left) © CanaPress Photo Service/Denis Paquin, (bottom) © Tom Thomson; p. 136 courtesy of Calgary Flames Limited Partnership; pp. 138-139 Kathryn Hollinrake; p. 141 courtesy of Provincial Archives of Manitoba, Floods 1930, 156; p. 142 © Doug Dealey; p. 143 (top) courtesy of Canada Centre for Remote Sensing, (bottom) © Tom Thomson; pp. 144-145 © Mike Grandmaison; pp. 146-150 courtesy of Kathleen Easton and Gorden Chorney; p. 152 © Tom Thomson; p. 153 Mike Blake/*Maclean's*; pp. 154-156 Phil Snel/*Maclean's*; p. 157 © Tom Thomson; p. 162 CanaPress Photo Service/Scot Takushi; p. 165 Reuters/NASA/Archive Photos; p. 168 Bill Sandford/*Toronto Sun*; p. 169 courtesy of Photofest © Walt Disney; pp. 175, 177-179 Dave Starrett; p. 183 CanaPress Photo Service/Denis Paquin; pp. 182-184 courtesy of Magellan Entertainment Group Inc.; p. 185 © Warren Toda/*Toronto Sun*

Illustrations
Cover: (top) Todd Ryoji, (bottom) Steve Attoe; pp. 6-7 Steve Attoe; pp. 8-10 Tina Holdcroft; pp. 13-14, 16-17, 19 Tadeusz Majewski; pp. 21-25 Laszlo Gal; pp. 27-28, 31-32, 36 Odile Ouellet; p. 37 Cover from "Little by Little" by Jean Little. Copyright © Jean Little, 1987. Reprinted by permission of Penguin Books Canada Limited; p. 39 Sean Dawdy; p. 40 Janet Wilson; p. 41 Barbara Spurll; pp. 43-46 Bernadette Lau; pp. 49, 51-52, 54 Stephen Snider; pp. 57, 59, 61, 63 Karen Reczuch; pp. 64-71 Don Kilby; pp. 72-75 Jun Park; pp. 79, 81-82 Celia Godkin; p. 85 Bart Vallecoccia; p. 86 Andrew Woodhouse; pp. 96-100 Bart Vallecoccia; pp. 115-117 Angela Vaculik; pp. 120-125 Scott Cameron; pp. 126-129 Jun Park; pp. 132-137 Steve MacEachern; pp. 141-142 Bart Vallecoccia; p. 166 courtesy of MET-TECH © 1997; p. 168 © Ingrid Rice/Vancouver; p. 169 courtesy of United Media; pp. 170-173 Scot Ritchie; pp. 182-184 courtesy of Magellan Entertainment Group Inc.

Text
"Decisions to Grow On" adapted from "Are You a Good Friend? by *Kid City* magazine. Copyright © 1994 Children's Television Workshop (New York, New York). All rights reserved. "Fifteen Minutes" by Larry Callen. From WHO KIDNAPPED THE SHERIFF by Larry Callen. Copyright © 1985 by Larry Callen. By permission of Little, Brown and Co. "Liam McLafferty's Choice" by Alexis O'Neill. Reprinted by permission of CRICKET magazine, April 1997, Vol. 24, No. 8, © 1997 by Alexis O'Neill. "The Grade Five Lie" by Jean Little. From *Little by Little* by Jean Little. Copyright © Jean Little, 1987. Reprinted by permission of Penguin Books Canada Limited. "About the Author" adapted from "Jean Little, Author" from the book *Writing Stories, Making Pictures: 150 Biographies of Canadian Children's Authors and Illustrators.* Copyright © 1994, the Canadian Children's Book Centre, Toronto. "No Matter ... " by Robert Priest. *From A Terrible Case of the Stars* by Robert Priest. Copyright © Robert Priest, 1994. Reprinted by permission of Penguin Books Canada Limited. "I Do Not Wish to Go to School" from A PIZZA THE SIZE OF THE SUN by Jack Prelutsky. Copyright © 1994, 1996 by Jack Prelutsky. By permission of Greenwillow Books, a division of William Morrow & Company, Inc. "Karate Kid" by Jane Yolen. From "Opening Days: Sports Poems," Harcourt Brace & Co., 1996. "Quitter" by Janet S. Wong.